SRA OPEN COURT READING

Comprehension and Language Arts Skills

Level 2

Annotated Teacher's Edition

A Division of The McGraw·Hill Companies

Columbus, Ohio

www.sra4kids.com

SRA/McGraw-Hill

A Division of The **McGraw·Hill** Companies

Send all inquiries to:
SRA/McGraw-Hill
8787 Orion Place
Columbus, OH 43240-4027

Printed in the United States of America

ISBN 0-07-571903-7

5 6 7 8 9 POH 06 05

Table of Contents

Unit 5 Courage

Unit 6 Our Country and Its People

Common and Proper Nouns

Nouns name persons, places, or things.

Rule	**Example**
▶ A **common noun** names a person, place, thing, or idea. Common nouns do not begin with a capital letter.	▶ dancer, country, car, color, happiness
▶ A **proper noun** names a certain person, place, or thing. Proper nouns begin with a capital letter.	▶ Dr. Green, America, English

Try It!

Underline the proper nouns in each sentence.

1. We saw a white tiger at the <u>Columbus Zoo</u>.

2. Tigers live in <u>Asia</u>.

3. Black leopards are found in the <u>Far East</u>.

4. The <u>Ringling Brothers Circus</u> has lions and tigers.

5. <u>Ziggy</u>, the zookeeper, feeds the big cats.

6. <u>Aunt Sue</u> said that tigers are bigger than lions.

Common and Proper Nouns

Read the story below. Underline the common nouns.

My <u>name</u> is Lara. I am a <u>tiger</u> from Russia. The <u>zoo</u> where I was born sent me to my new <u>home</u> in California. At first I was homesick, but now I like San Diego. I can smell the Pacific Ocean when I wake up.

Proofread

Read the paragraph below. Underline with three lines (≡) letters that need to be capitalized.

We went to the zoo in f̲lorida on s̲aturday. We saw six elephants and two giraffes. I liked the zebra named z̲ig z̲ag. My brother liked the birds the best. There was a parrot named b̲ill. I love going to the zoo.

GRAMMAR AND USAGE

Compare and Contrast

Focus   Writers sometimes use comparison in a story to make an idea clearer.

> ▶ To **compare** means to tell how things, events, or characters are **alike** in some way.
> ▶ To **contrast** means to tell how things, events, or characters are **different.**
> ▶ Clue words help show how things are alike and different:
>
>
>
> **Clue Words**
>
>
>
> | **Alike** | | **Different** |
> |---|---|---|
> | both | as | different |
> | same | too | but |
> | like | | |

Identify

1. Read page 26 of "Come Back, Jack!" What comparision is made between the little girl

   and the rest of her family? <u>Her family likes books, but</u>

   <u>the little girl does not.</u>

2. Read page 29 of "Come Back, Jack!" What did the little girl and Jack do that is alike? <u>They both</u>

   <u>crawled inside the book.</u>

▶ **Compare and Contrast**

 **Practice**

Circle whether the sentence is comparing or contrasting. Write the clue word on the line.

3. Jack went into the castle. Jill went into the castle too.

(Compare) Contrast <u>too</u>

4. The little girl laughed, just like Jack.

(Compare) Contrast <u>like</u>

 **Apply**

Think about "Come Back, Jack!" List one way that Jack and his sister are alike.

5. <u>Sentence will vary.</u>

_____

List one way that Jack and his sister are different.

6. <u>Sentence will vary.</u>

_____

COMPREHENSION

Subject and Object Pronouns

Subject pronouns take the place of the subject of a sentence. **Object pronouns** take the place of the object of a sentence.

Rule	**Example**
▶The subject pronouns are: Singular: I, you, he, she, it Plural: we, you, they	▶I know that dogs and wolves are related. **They** are both good hunters.
▶The object pronouns are: Singular: me, you, him, her, it Plural: us, you, them	▶My dog will like **you.** The puppies made **us** laugh every day.

Write a pronoun to replace the underlined nouns in each sentence.

1. <u>Clara Barton</u> was a teacher in New Jersey. ____She____

2. <u>You and I</u> know that she founded the Red Cross. ____We____

3. The Red Cross helped <u>my family</u>. ____us____

GRAMMAR AND USAGE

▶ Subject and Object Pronouns

Practice

Circle the subject pronouns and underline the object pronouns in the paragraph.

My name is James Cook, and (I) am a sailor. In 1768, (I) became the captain of a ship. (I) burned vinegar and gunpowder on my ship, because (they) purified the air. (I) made the sailors eat fruit to help them stay healthy. (They) thanked me for caring about them.

Proofread

Read the paragraph, and replace each underlined noun with the proper subject or object pronoun.

Christopher Columbus sailed to America, and

Christopher Columbus ___he___ started

colonies there. Many explorers traveled across

the Atlantic Ocean, and the explorers ___they___

saw new lands. We read about the explorers

___them___ in history books.

Name _____ Date _____

Time and Order Words

You can tell when something happens by using time and order words in your writing.

Rule
▶ Words such as *yesterday*, *tonight*, and *next week* show time.

Example
▶ We can see Polaris, the North Star, **tonight.**

You can show how something happens by using order words.

▶ Words such as *first*, *next*, and *finally* show order.

▶ **First,** place your apples in the basket. **Then** weigh them on the scale.

 **Write the time or order word from each sentence on the line.**

1. Yesterday, we learned about our history. _yesterday_

2. First, we learned that the first president served in 1789. _first_

3. Tomorrow, we will study the states. _tomorrow_

4. I will read more about history tonight for homework. _tonight_

▶ **Time and Order Words**

Practice

Underline the time and order words in each sentence.

5. <u>Tomorrow</u>, my class will talk about our pets.

6. <u>Tonight</u> I will write what I want to say.

7. <u>First</u>, I will tell my pet's name.

8. <u>Then</u>, I will say that he is a dog.

9. <u>Finally</u>, I will show a picture of my pet.

10. <u>After school</u>, I will take my dog for a walk.

WRITER'S CRAFT

UNIT I   Sharing Stories • **Lesson 3** *The Library*

Action Verbs

An **action verb** tells what someone is doing.

Rule	**Example**
▶ Words that name an action are called action verbs.	▶ We **played** in the park for two hours.

 **Try It!**

Circle the action verb in each sentence.

1. We (drove) for eight hours.

2. I (slept) for three hours.

3. Then I (read) a book for one hour.

4. We (ate) lunch at 12:00 noon.

5. At night, we (walked) by the lake.

▶ **Action Verbs**

GRAMMAR AND USAGE

Practice

Read the paragraph below. Write an action verb in each blank.

On Saturday, we ___**went**___ to the

swimming pool. I ___**like**___ to swim.

Sometimes I ___**dive**___ for pennies on

the bottom of the pool. The lifeguard

___**watched/saw**___ me swim. I ___**wanted**___

to swim all day.

Proofread

Read the story below. Circle the best action verb for each sentence.

Ice hockey players (**wear**) **have** ice skates.
They (**glide**) **are** across the ice when they
play. The goalkeeper **has** (**blocks**) the puck.
He must (**move**) **be** fast. Two defenders
(**play**) **are** on each side of the goalkeeper.
They (**help**) **are** the goalkeeper.

Effective Beginnings and Endings

A good beginning grabs your reader's attention. Then your reader will want to read the rest of your story.

A good ending tells the reader how the story ends. It is important to have a good ending for everything you write.

This beginning can be made better. Write a better beginning on the lines.

There was a boy. He lived in the United States. He was young. His younger sister gave him a present.

Better beginnings should include

some of the following: dialogue,

asking questions, or adding details.

Effective Beginnings and Endings

This ending needs improvement. Write a better ending on the lines.

The gift was very special to him. He put it away in his closet. The end.

Students should include some

excitement, concluding details, or

question/answer sequences.

WRITER'S CRAFT

Following Clues

Focus   Sometimes a writer does not tell the reader everything. Sometimes a writer leaves clues for the reader to follow.

> ▶ Information in a story gives the reader a clue.
> ▶ Clues can help you learn more about a story's characters. For example, *Gwen put on her golden crown.* You can figure out from this sentence that Gwen is probably a queen or princess.

Identify

Read each sentence below. Then look in "Story Hour—Starring Megan!" for clues that help you know the characters better.

1. Megan really wants to learn to read. What clue tells you?

   She tries to read everywhere she goes.

2. Megan knew Andrew was there before she saw him. What clue told her?

   a stuffed dinosaur

Name _____ Date _____

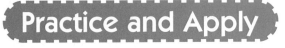

Practice and Apply

Read the paragraphs below. Then answer
the questions.

Megan takes Alfred for a walk every day.
When they get home, Megan feeds and waters
Alfred. Then she brushes his shiny fur. Alfred
barks his thanks.

What is Alfred? __A dog_____

What clues tell you that? __He has fur. He barks.__

__Megan walks and feeds him.__

_____

Yesterday, Bert had trouble getting to
school on time. First he could not find his
boots. Then he could not find his mittens.
When he finally got his coat, hat, and scarf
on, the bus was waiting for him.

What is the weather like? __cold_____

What clues tell you that? __Bert had to wear boots,__

__mittens, a coat, a hat, and a scarf.__

_____

COMPREHENSION

Possessive Nouns and Possessive Pronouns

Possessive words show ownership.

Rule	Example
▶ A **possessive noun** ends in an apostrophe *s* or just an apostrophe (').	▶ Singular: Megan**'s** mother works at the library. Plural: The girls' dresses were green.
▶ A **possessive pronoun** takes the place of a possessive noun. There is no apostrophe at the end.	▶ Singular: **Her** mother works at the library. Plural: **Their** books are over there.

Try It!

Write the possessive pronoun that would replace the underlined noun.

1. Megan's brother is Nathan. ___Her___

2. The book's cover was colorful. ___Its___

3. He brought Andrew's book to the library. ___his___

4. I want to borrow Megan's and Martin's book.

   ___their___

UNIT I Sharing Stories • **Lesson 4** *Story Hour—Starring Megan!*

Possessive Nouns and Possessive Pronouns

 **Practice**

Write the possessive form of the noun at the end of each sentence.

5. ___Jeff's___ favorite is mystery. [Jeff]

6. I read my ___friend's___ comic books. [friend]

7. What is ___your___ favorite book? [you]

8. The ___books'___ covers were torn. [books]

9. The ___librarian's___ suggestion was very helpful. [librarian]

Proofread

Read the paragraph below. Change any underlined possessive pronouns that are wrong. Write the correct word above the incorrect word.

   Did you like <u>mine</u> book *Runie the Unicorn*?
 my

<u>My</u> mother's friend gave it to me for <u>mine</u>
          my

birthday. <u>Hers</u> favorite part is when the unicorn
 Her

finds the magic crystal in the forest. <u>My</u> favorite

part is when the little girl helps the unicorn. I

didn't ruin the ending, did I?

GRAMMAR AND USAGE

Staying on Topic

You should always stay on your topic when you write. Going off the topic will confuse your reader.

One way to stay on your topic is to make a plan before you write. Putting your ideas in a graphic organizer is a good way to plan.

When you revise your writing, ask these questions to be sure you are staying on the topic.

▶ Did I tell my topic near the beginning of the paragraph?

▶ Do I have any details that aren't needed?

 **Read the sentences below. Cross out the sentences that do not stay on the topic.**

Topic: Doctors help people in many ways.

1. Doctors give people medicine to cure sickness.

2. ~~Some doctors work in hospitals.~~

3. Doctors can operate to heal people.

4. Doctors give shots to stop sickness.

5. ~~Doctors and nurses work together.~~

▶ **Staying on Topic**

Practice

**Write sentences that go with each topic
sentence. Write the sentences on the lines.**

6. Dogs make good pets.

Answers will vary.
_____

_____

_____

7. There are good reasons to play sports.

Answers will vary.
_____

_____

_____

8. There are many ways to get to school.

Answers will vary.
_____

_____

_____

WRITER'S CRAFT

Viewpoint of a Story

Focus   When a story is told by a character in the story, readers see the story through the eyes of that character. The storyteller will use words like *I* and *me*. This is called **first-person point of view.** When the story is told by someone who is not part of the story, then the storyteller uses words like *he*, *she*, and *it*. This is called **third-person point of view.**

Identify

Look at the story "Tomás and the Library Lady." What is the point of view? <u>third-person point of view</u>

How do you know? <u>The storyteller uses words like</u> *he* and *she*.

Practice

Find your favorite book.

Title: <u>Answers will vary.</u>

Story's point of view: _____

How do you know? _____

_____

▶**Viewpoint of a Story**

Write a short paragraph about something that happened in school from first-person point of view. Then rewrite the paragraph from third-person point of view. Perhaps you could use your teacher's viewpoint.

Answers will vary.

_____

_____

_____

_____

_____

_____

_____

_____

_____

_____

COMPREHENSION

Review

▶ Proper Nouns

**Read the sentences below. Circle the
proper nouns.**

1. (Carol) and (Tracie) are pals.

2. They are going to (Florida) in (December).

3. Every winter, they go to the (Miami Zoo).

4. (Jimmy) the polar bear is always sleeping.

5. See you next (Monday)!

▶ Possessive Nouns and Pronouns

**Correct any incorrect possessive nouns
or pronouns. Write the word on the line.**

6. **Mine** computer is not working! _____My_____

7. The **computers** screen is blank. __computer's__

8. Is **you're** computer working? _____your_____

9. Maybe I will ask **our's** teacher to help. _____our_____

10. We can use **hers** computer. _____her_____

▶ **Review**

GRAMMAR AND USAGE

▶ **Subject and Object Pronouns**

Underline the subject pronouns and circle the object pronouns in these sentences.

11. When will <u>she</u> come to visit?

12. Her letter will tell (you) the date.

13. <u>It</u> will give the time of day, also.

14. The van will meet (them) at the airport.

15. <u>She</u> will bring (me) a present.

▶ **Verbs**

Add an action verb to each sentence.

16. The rocket ___**blasted**___ off into space.

17. How long would it ___**fly**___ around Earth?

18. Rockets ___**carry**___ their own fuel.

19. The blast-off ___**made**___ so much noise!

20. Men, women, and dogs can ___**travel**___ in space shuttles.

UNIT 2 Kindness • **Lesson 1** *Mushroom in the Rain*

Drawing Conclusions

Focus Readers get ideas, or draw conclusions, about what is happening in a story by using clues from the story.

Read pages 112 and 113 of "Mushroom in the Rain." What clue lets you know that the animals are learning that they can make a little more room under the mushroom?

They let the rabbit in without asking, "How can

we let you in?"

Look through "Mushroom in the Rain" to find information the writer gives about the mushroom. On the following lines, write what the information tells you about mushrooms. If you already know something about mushrooms that helps you understand how the mushroom was able to grow so big, put that information in what you write, too.

Answers will vary.

UNIT 2 Kindness • **Lesson 1** *Mushroom in the Rain*

▶ Drawing Conclusions

Read the sentences below. Then use what they tell you to draw a conclusion.

- The classes at the town's dance school are always full.
- Many people watch when the dance students perform.
- Most children in the town say they want to study dance.
- The dance school is moving to a bigger building next year.

Conclusion ___These people like dance._____

_____

_____

_____

COMPREHENSION

Capitalization: Beginnings of Sentences

Capital letters can be used in many places. One place capital letters are used is at the beginning of a sentence.

Rule	Example
▶ A sentence always begins with a capital letter.	▶ Camping is fun. **Have** you ever slept outside?

Try It!

Underline three times (☰) the beginning letter of each sentence.

<u>w</u>ho uses x-ray machines? <u>d</u>octors use x-ray machines to look inside your body. <u>d</u>entists also use x-ray machines to check your teeth and gums. <u>a</u>irports use x-ray machines to check luggage for any dangerous metal objects. <u>a</u>n x-ray machine makes a picture on a piece of film.

MECHANICS

Capitalization: Beginnings of Sentences

Underline three times (≡) the letters that should be capital letters in the paragraph below.

butterflies hatch as caterpillars. later, they come out of their cocoons as beautiful butterflies. butterflies come out during the day. there are about 15,000 kinds of butterflies. what is your favorite kind of butterfly?

Proofread

Underline three times (≡) the letters that should be capital letters.

Dear Butterfly,

today, I saw you flying. where were you going? you flew by yesterday at the same time! I would like to know where you were headed. maybe you were going to have your lunch. thank you for flying by and letting me see your pretty wings.

Sincerely,
A Butterfly Fan

Tone of a Personal Letter

Tone tells how the writer feels about something. You should think about tone when you write.

In a personal letter, the tone is usually friendly.

Dear Sara,
   How have you been? I am great. I can't wait until you visit! I'll see you soon.

Your friend,

Nicki

Try It! **Write *friendly* next to the sentences that have a friendly tone.**

1. Thank you for the nice gift. _friendly_____

2. Don't call me again! _____

3. It is good to see you again. _friendly_____

4. You hurt my feelings. _____

5. How can I help you? ___friendly_____

▶**Tone of a Personal Letter**

Practice

Write a short letter to a friend. Be sure your letter has a friendly tone.

Answers will vary.

_____

_____

_____

_____

_____

WRITER'S CRAFT

Sequence

Focus Sequence is the order in which things happen in a story. The more you know about when things happen in a story, the better you can understand the story.

> Some sequence clue words tell
> ▶ the **order** in which things happen
>   *first, then, finally*
> ▶ the **time** or when things happen
>   *tonight, in the morning, once upon a time*

Identify

Look through "The Elves and the Shoemaker" for examples of sequence words.

1. Circle the kind of sequence words the writer uses most often.

   • (time)   • order

2. List four examples of sequence words or phrases from the story.

   Answers will vary. _____   _____

   _____   _____

▶ Sequence

COMPREHENSION

Practice and Apply

Write a story about what you did in school today. Use sequence words to tell the time and order of your story.

Stories will vary.

_____

_____

_____

_____

_____

_____

_____

Name _____   Date _____

Commas: Greetings and Closings

Commas are used in different ways. One way is in friendly letters.

Rule
▶ Write a comma after the name in the greeting of a friendly letter.
▶ Write a comma after the closing of a friendly letter.

Example
▶Dear Cinderella,

▶Love,
Prince Charming

Try It!

Read this letter and put a comma (,) where needed.

Dear Rapunzel,
    I have heard that you have the longest hair in the kingdom. Why is the prince climbing up your hair? Isn't it time you had the elevator fixed?

                    Your friend,
                    Sleeping Beauty

UNIT 2 Kindness • **Lesson 2** *The Elves and the Shoemaker*

▶ **Commas: Greetings and Closings**

 **Practice**

Write commas in the list of possible greetings and closings for a friendly letter.

1. Dear Oscar,

2. Respectfully,
   Oliver

3. Best wishes,
   Nolah

4. My dear Nina,

5. Dearest Maria,

6. Love,
   Mario

 **Proofread**

Add commas where they are needed. Use proofreading marks.

Dear Sleeping Beauty,

   The prince only climbed up my hair once. He was in a hurry. It was an emergency. A dragon was chasing him! (We finally got the elevator fixed!)

                    Sincerely,
                    Rapunzel,

MECHANICS

Sentence Elaboration

Add more details to your sentences to make your writing better.

Rule

▶ Add words that tell where or when.

▶ Add words that put a picture in the reader's mind.

▶ Combine sentences that go together.

Example

▶ Dinosaurs lived a long time ago.
With details: Many dinosaurs lived in South America over 65 million years ago.

▶ Dinosaurs were big.
With details: Dinosaurs were giant creatures that were over 20 feet tall.

▶ Dinosaurs are a mystery. Scientists study fossils.
With details: Scientists study fossils because dinosaurs are a mystery.

Try It! **Circle the words that add detail in each sentence.**

1. The peacock had (bright) feathers.

2. The zoo opened (in 1875) (down the street).

3. The (wild) cheetah ran (swiftly).

4. Our class went to the zoo (because we were) (studying tigers).

Comprehension and Language Arts Skills

UNIT 2   Kindness • **Lesson 2** *The Elves and the Shoemaker*

▶ **Sentence Elaboration**

Practice

Rewrite these sentences adding details.

5. My friend is great.

Answers will vary. _____

6. The rabbits were found.

Answers will vary. _____

7. Adam went to Texas. His aunt lives out west.

Answers will vary. _____

8. The men helped the family.

Answers will vary. _____

9. Shoes are nice.

Answers will vary. _____

WRITER'S CRAFT

Name _____ Date _____

Capitalization: Names of Days, Names of Months, and Greetings of Letters

There are several rules for capitalization. Calendars will help you remember to capitalize the days of the week and the months of the year. You must also remember to capitalize the first word of your greeting in a personal letter.

Rule	**Example**
▶ Days of the week begin with a capital letter.	▶ Sunday
▶ Months of the year begin with a capital letter.	▶ October
▶ Capitalize the first letter of a greeting.	▶ Dear Rolo,

Try It!

Write the name of the day or the month in each sentence below.

1. The day before Wednesday is __Tuesday__.

2. New Year's Day is the first of __January__.

3. The last day of the year is in __December__.

4. The day before Friday is __Thursday__.

Capitalization: Names of Days, Names of Months, and Greetings of Letters

 **Practice**

**Read this letter. Underline three times
(≡) each letter that should be capitalized.**

friday, may 4, 2003

dear Gretel,
    I have finally learned the number of days in
the months.

Thirty days has september,
april, june, and november;
All the rest have thirty-one.
february has twenty-eight alone;
Save in leap year, at which time,
february's days are twenty-nine.

Love,
Hansel

Proofread

**Read this letter. Underline three times
(≡) letters that should be capitalized.**

wednesday, november 7, 2003

dear Jimmy,
    Last october, my family went to the zoo. In
november, we are going to my aunt's farm.

Sincerely,
Sam

MECHANICS

UNIT 2 **Kindness • Lesson 3** *The Paper Crane*

Structure of a Personal Letter

When you write a personal letter, make sure you have all the parts.

1. Heading
2. Greeting
3. Body
4. Closing
5. Your name

Dear Martin,

   I'm glad you could come and visit. It was great to see you. I had fun at the fair.

                        Your friend,

                        Julia

Try It! **Write what part is shown on the line next to it.**

123 Main Street
Town, State 12344 _____heading_____

Dear Anne, _____greeting_____

   Thank you for coming to my party. _____body_____
I had so much fun.

_____closing_____ Yours truly,

_____name_____ Alice

UNIT 2 Kindness • **Lesson 3** *The Paper Crane*

Structure of a Personal Letter

Practice

Write a letter to a friend or relative. Make sure you include all the parts.

Answers will vary. _____

_____

_____

_____

_____

_____

_____

_____

_____

_____

WRITER'S CRAFT

Commas: Words in a Series

There are many places to use commas. One place they are used is in a list of things.

Rule	**Example**
▶ A comma is used after each item in a series or list of things except the last one.	▶ My sister went to see an ear, nose, and throat doctor.

Try It!

Commas have been left out in the sentences below. Put commas where they are needed in the lists.

1. Fleas, flies, and bees drive me crazy!

2. Insects eat things such as wood, paper, and even other insects.

3. Bats, birds, and reptiles also eat insects.

4. What is red, juicy, and healthy? An apple!

Commas: Words in a Series

MECHANICS

Practice

Find each sentence that has commas in the right place. Circle the letter in front of it.

5. (a.) Cars can be red, blue, black, or green.
   b. Trees can be tall short, thin or wide.

6. (a.) The American flag is red, white, and blue.
   b. The Italian flag is red white, and green.

7. (a.) Bread, milk, and eggs are good for you.
   b. Bread can be white rye or, whole wheat.

8. a. Are football, basketball, and baseball, alike?
   (b.) Are swimming, diving, and ice skating alike?

Proofread

Read the story and add commas where they are needed. Use proofreading marks.

    Flowers have soft petals‚ pretty colors‚ and a nice smell. To grow flowers‚ you must plant the seeds‚ water the plants‚ and pull the weeds. Flowers look pretty in a garden‚ in your office‚ or in your house. Today, we will plant purple pansies‚ white daisies‚ and lilies all around the border of the garden.

Time and Order Words

You can show time in your writing by telling when things happen.

▶ Words like *today* and *next week* show time.

▶ You can show order by telling in what order things happen.

▶ Words like *first*, *next*, and *finally* show order.

Try It!

Underline the time and order words in each sentence.

1. The race was <u>yesterday</u>.

2. It took place <u>in the afternoon</u>.

3. Amanda was the <u>first</u> to cross the finish line.

4. <u>Last year</u>, she came in <u>third</u>.

5. Pete was the <u>second</u> one to finish.

6. Tony was the <u>last</u> runner.

UNIT 2 Kindness • **Lesson 4** *Butterfly House*

▶ **Time and Order Words**

WRITER'S CRAFT

Practice

Find the time and order words in the paragraph. Circle the time and order words.

(Last summer) my family went camping. (When) we got to the campsite, we set up our tent. (First) we put posts in the ground. (Then) we tied ropes from the posts to the tent. (Finally) we put poles in the middle of the tent to hold it up. (That night) we built a fire and told stories. It was so much fun. We plan to go again (next year).

Making Inferences

Focus   Instead of telling you everything, writers sometimes just give you clues.

> Information in a story gives the reader a clue. Clues can help you know more about things that happen in a story.

Identify

Read page 180 of "Corduroy." Circle the sentence that is true.

- (Corduroy hopes that a shopper will buy him.)
- Corduroy hopes that a shopper doesn't buy him.

What clues let you know? Day after day he waited; the store was filled with shoppers, but no one ever seemed to want a small bear.

Practice

Read each sentence below. Write clues from the sentence that tell what happened. Then write what that clue tells you.

1. Lin was out of breath as she told the teacher about finding someone's glasses on the playground.

Clue Lin was out of breath.

What the clue tells you: She ran to the teacher.

UNIT 2 Kindness • **Lesson 5** *Corduroy*

▶Making Inferences

2. Jacob covered his ears when he heard his brother's music playing.

Clue: **Jacob covered his ears.**

What the clue tells you: **Either he did not like the music or it was too loud.**

Write a paragraph about a game you like to play or a game you don't like to play without telling whether you like the game or not. Let your readers use the clues to figure out how you feel about the game.

Paragraphs will vary.

_____

_____

_____

_____

_____

_____

Comprehension and Language Arts Skills

UNIT 2 • Lesson 5 **45**

COMPREHENSION

Quotation Marks and Underlining

Quotation marks and **underlining** are types of punctuation used in good writing.

Rule	Example
▶Quotation marks are used right before and right after the words a speaker says.	▶"There's fire in my mouth," the dragon said.
▶Quotation marks are used around the titles of stories, poems, and book chapters.	▶I like the story "Snow White and the Seven Dwarves."
▶The title of a book or movie is underlined.	▶Robert Louis Stevenson wrote <u>Treasure Island</u>.

 **Try It!**

Read the sentences below. Add quotation marks or underlining where needed.

1. The Mad Hatter said,"Digital watches are best."

2."Don't eat so fast!"exclaimed Little Red Riding Hood.

3."The Cat Who Became a Poet"is a funny story.

Quotation Marks and Underlining

Write quotation marks where they belong in each sentence.

4. "What's in a name?" Shakespeare asked.

5. The poet Virgil said, "We can't all do everything."

6. "There's the very bear I've always wanted," said Goldilocks.

7. My mom said, "Have a nice day!"

Underline the titles of movies or books, and put the titles of poems and stories in quotation marks.

8. My favorite book is <u>The House at Pooh Corner</u>.

9. Have you ever read <u>Now We Are Six</u>?

10. No, but now I'm reading the story "Ant and the Three Little Figs."

11. My sister likes the poem "Books to the Ceiling" best.

MECHANICS

Sensory Details

Descriptions make a picture in the reader's mind. Good describing words help readers see, hear, feel, smell, or taste things the writer tells them about.

▶ The sparkling, white snow was wet and cold. Don't eat the snow! It's too salty!

Try It!

Circle the describing words in each sentence.

1. The kitten had (soft) fur.

2. We saw a (large), (blue), (round) object in the road.

3. The food tastes (salty) and (spicy).

4. The music was (loud).

5. The candle gave off a (sweet) smell.

Name _____   Date _____

▶**Sensory Details**

Practice

Read the paragraph below. Circle the words that give sensory detail.

As I went into the movie theater, my nose filled with the smell of (sweet) popcorn. I could hear (loud) voices coming from the movies. There was (happy) music playing in the lobby. I sat down in the (soft) seat and began to eat my popcorn. It was (buttery) and (salty). The (red) curtains finally opened to a (huge) screen. The movie was about to begin.

Commas: Cities, States, and Dates

You can use commas when writing names of cities and states, and in dates.

Rule	**Example**
▶Use a comma between the city and state names in the heading of a letter.	▶Venice, California
▶Use a comma between the day and year when writing the date in a letter.	▶May 31, 2003

Try It!

Write commas where they belong.

1. 695 Beach Street
Seaside,California

2. April 14,1849

3. Denver,Colorado

4. January 31,1984

5. 1462 Bryden Road
Poland,Ohio

Commas: Cities, States, and Dates

MECHANICS

Read this paragraph. Write commas between each day and year, and between the names of cities and states.

The train arrived in Albany,New York on March 13,1997. It continued down the track until it reached Philadelphia,Pennsylvania. It was sidetracked there until March 15,1997. The train finally arrived in Baltimore,Maryland on March 19,1997. From there, the train brought the president home to the White House.

Add six commas where they are needed in the paragraph below. Use proofreading marks.

My class was studying unusual names of cities in the United States. I began my report on February 6,2003. I read about Boulder, Colorado. I wonder if the rocks in that city are bigger than the rocks in Little Rock,Arkansas. Do buffaloes really live in Buffalo,New York? Does everyone sew in Needles,California? I finished my report on February 12,2003.

Structure of a Business Letter

A business letter has six parts.
1. Heading: Your address
2. Inside Address: Name and address of the person to whom you are writing; include date
3. Greeting: Usually *Dear* and the person's name to whom you are writing
4. Body: This is where you tell what you want.
5. Closing: Usually *Sincerely* or *Thank you*
6. Signature: Write your first and last name.

Try It! **Read the letter. Label the parts.**

152 Cherry Ln. <u>heading</u>
Cleveland, OH 44051

Ms. Perry <u>inside address</u>
1462 Bryden Road
Columbus, Ohio 43205
February 21, 2004

Dear Ms. Perry: <u>greeting</u>

   The computer game I got from your company <u>body</u>
didn't work. Please send me another game.

<u>closing</u> Thank you,

<u>signature</u> Dan Danson

► **Structure of a Business Letter**

Write a business letter that asks a local museum for information. Be sure to include all six parts.

Heading
_____

_____

Inside address
_____

_____

_____

Greeting
_____

Body
_____

_____

_____

Closing
_____

Signature
_____

WRITER'S CRAFT

▶ Capitalization

Make sure you use capital letters, commas, and punctuation marks correctly. They all help make writing clear for the reader.

Underline three times (☰) the letters in the following sentences that need to be capitalized.

1. thank-you notes thank people for things they have done.

2. last september, we visited my cousins in Maryland.

3. dear Charley,

4. on sundays, we write letters.

5. We mail them on monday.

►Review

MECHANICS

►Commas

Read the letter below. Write commas where they are needed, and underline three times the letters that should be capital letters.

sunday, november 16

dear Irina,

we had such a good time at your birthday party on friday. thank you for inviting us. My sister and I liked the games, the movie, and the cake.

Best wishes,
Lana

►Punctuation

Read the invitation below. Insert two pairs of quotation marks. Underline two movie titles, and underline three times two letters that should be capitalized.

Movie Show
saturday, october 25
2:00 p.m.
Dru and Sue say, "Come one, come all!"
Special movie showing of
Cinderella in Space and
Prince Charming Goes to Mars
Call us at 432–1865 and say "Yes!"

UNIT 2 Kindness • **Lesson 7** *Cinderella*

Background Information

Tell your reader facts about a person, place, or event. This will help your reader better understand what you want to say.

▶ I like my new school better than my old school.
With background information: I like my new school better than my old school because my old school didn't have a tennis team.

 **Try It!** **Underline the background information in each sentence.**

1. It is amazing my dog can run so well. <u>He got hit by a car two months ago.</u>

2. The day I didn't get picked for the football team was a good day. <u>I ended up trying out for the baseball team and I made it!</u>

3. My sister is very smart. <u>She can read.</u> <u>She is three years old.</u>

4. My grandma's dark, dusty attic is a great place. <u>It has old boxes filled with treasures.</u>

5. The ski trip was fun. <u>We skied down a huge mountain, then we drank hot chocolate.</u>

►**Background Information**

Give background information about these topics.

6. Second grade is better than first grade.

Answers will vary.

_____

_____

7. My last school trip was fun.

Answers will vary.

_____

_____

8. My family lives downtown.

Answers will vary.

_____

_____

WRITER'S CRAFT

Kinds of Sentences

There are different kinds of sentences.

Rule	**Example**
▶A **declarative sentence** makes a statement. It always ends with a period (.).	▶Mars is a planet.
▶An **interrogative sentence** asks a question. It always ends in a question mark (?).	▶Will people ever live on Mars?
▶An **imperative sentence** gives directions or a command. It always ends in a period (.).	▶Begin the countdown now.
▶An **exclamatory sentence** shows strong feelings. It always ends with an exclamation mark (!).	▶What a perfect launch!

Try It!

Read each sentence below. Write the type of sentence on the line.

1. Go outside and build a snowman. __imperative__

2. Then, mother said, "Wear your cap, Stan!" __exclamatory__

UNIT 3 Look Again • **Lesson 1** *I See Animals Hiding*

▶ **Kinds of Sentences**

Put the correct end mark at the end of each sentence.

1. Where does snow come from?

2. Icy droplets of water in clouds turn into snowflakes.

3. It's amazing that no two snowflakes are alike!

4. Where do the water droplets come from?

5. They come from Earth's lakes, rivers, and oceans.

Read the paragraph below. Insert end marks where they belong. Use proofreading marks.

What can change in a minute or stay the same for months at a time? The weather! The tropics are hot areas of the world. In the tropics, the weather doesn't change for months at a time. In some parts of the world, storms can change a sunny day into a rainy day. Trying to figure out what the weather will be is a difficult job.

GRAMMAR AND USAGE

Organizing Expository Writing

> ▶ Expository writing gives facts. Expository writing is not make-believe.
> ▶ Start your expository paragraph with your topic. Then add details. End with a sentence that sums up your main points.
>
> Here are some tips to organize your details:
> ▶ Put the most important facts first.
> ▶ List in the order in which things happen.

 **Read these statements. Write *true* if the statement is true. Write *make-believe* if the statement is make-believe.**

1. The firefighters put out the fire.

true
_____

2. My dog called the fire department.

make-believe
_____

3. The family woke up to the smoke alarms.

true
_____

4. All of the aliens were safe.

make-believe
_____

Practice

Make a list of the things you do in a normal day at school.

Answers will vary.

_____

_____

_____

_____

Topic Sentences

A topic sentence tells the main idea of a paragraph. It is often the first sentence of a paragraph.

Topic Sentence: Exercise will change your life for the better.
This sentence tells the reader that the paragraph is going to be about exercise and how it will change your life.

 **Read the sentences below. Circle the topic sentence.**

1. Robinson was a major league baseball player.

2. He played for the Brooklyn Dodgers in 1946.

3. Jackie Robinson made history.

▶ Topic Sentences

Write a topic sentence for this paragraph.

Answers will vary.

_____

I learned about insects there. I also got a lot of exercise. I swam and hiked. I met some great new friends. I can't wait to go back to camp next summer.

Think about something you like to do or study. Write a topic sentence about it.

Answers will vary.

_____

_____

_____

WRITER'S CRAFT

Drawing Conclusions

Focus Thinking about the information in a story can help readers make decisions about what is happening.

> Readers can **draw conclusions** about a character or event in a story by using information in the story's words and pictures.

Identify

Read these sentences from "They Thought They Saw Him." Write the conclusion you can make from the underlined information in each sentence.

1. <u>All winter</u> little dark chameleon had lived, <u>safe and asleep</u>, beneath the granary where the people kept their seed corn.

Chameleons are not very active during

the winter.

2. As he moved on <u>quick silent feet</u>, he began to forget the sleepy winter dark and felt the joy in the first wakeful light of spring.

Possible answer: Chameleons become more

active in the spring.

Drawing Conclusions

Practice and Apply

Read the following paragraph. Then answer the questions below by drawing conclusions.

Our teacher, Ms. Smith, began talking to herself. "Now, where are they? I can't read without them." She looked through her desk drawers. She looked in her purse. She patted her pockets. As Ms. Smith scratched her head, we began to giggle. She found what she had been looking for. "I always leave them up there," she laughed.

What was Ms. Smith doing?

looking for her glasses
_____

_____

Why did the students giggle when Ms. Smith scratched her head?

They already knew where the glasses were.
_____

_____

COMPREHENSION

Linking Verbs and Helping Verbs

Sometimes verbs don't show action. These verbs are called linking and helping verbs.

Rule

▶ A **linking verb** joins, or connects, the parts of a sentence to make it complete.

▶ A **helping verb** helps the main verb in a sentence tell when something will happen, has happened, or is happening.

Example

▶ There **is** a pretty shell on the beach.

▶ We **are** planning to look for shells tomorrow.

 **Try It!**

Read each sentence. Write an *L* if the underlined verb is a linking verb. Write an *H* if the verb is a helping verb.

1. I <u>was</u> swimming like a fish today. __H__

2. Fish <u>have been</u> swimming in the oceans for

millions of years. __H__

3. The fish <u>was</u> cold. __L__

UNIT 3 Look Again • **Lesson 2** *They Thought They Saw Him*

Linking Verbs and Helping Verbs

Read the paragraph below. Underline the linking verbs. Circle the helping verbs.

There are more than 20,000 types of fish. I (have) eaten swordfish and sardines. (Have) you ever eaten eel? A shark is a very big fish. Are sea horses fish? The lionfish is orange.

Proofread

Read the paragraph below. Write in linking or helping verbs to complete the sentences.

There _____are_____ six fish in my aquarium.

The blue fish _____was/is_____ swimming faster

than the orange fish. My cat _____was/is_____

watching them swim. I _____have_____ tried

to teach the cat to behave. These fish

_____are_____ not for dinner, Miss Kitty!

GRAMMAR AND USAGE

Note Taking

Taking good notes helps you remember facts. These facts can help you write a good report. Remembering facts also helps you do well on tests.

Remember these tips to take good notes:
- ▶ Use a different page for each kind of information you collect.
- ▶ Make a heading for each kind of information. You may have many facts under one heading.
- ▶ Write your notes in your own words.
- ▶ Write down only the most important facts.
- ▶ Write neatly.

Try It! **Look at the topic below. Write some notes about things you know about it.**

The Moon

Answers may include: _____

is far away _____

looks blue in color _____

has deep craters _____

takes 27 days, 7 hours, and 43 minutes to orbit the earth. _____

▶ Note Taking

Read the paragraph below. Take notes on the information you read.

Earth is very interesting. It is made mostly of water. There are also forests and mountains on Earth's surface. It is 93 million miles from the sun, but we still feel the sun's heat. Earth takes one year to revolve around the sun. It rotates on its axis in one day.

Earth

made mostly of water

93 million miles from sun

one year to revolve around sun

one day to rotate on axis

WRITER'S CRAFT

Subject-Verb Agreement

A sentence has a subject and a verb that agree. This means that the subject and the verb must both be singular, or they must both be plural.

Rule
▶ If the subject of a sentence is singular, the verb must be singular.

▶ If the subject of a sentence is plural, the verb must be plural.

Example
▶ A **plant needs** air, sunlight, and water.

▶ **Plants need** warmth to grow.

Write *S* if the sentence has a singular subject and verb and *P* if the sentence has a plural subject and verb.

1. A house plant grows indoors. __S__

2. Herbs are plants used in cooking. __P__

3. Wildflowers grow by themselves outside. __P__

4. An evergreen tree keeps its leaves all year

   long. __S__

Name _____ Date _____

►Subject-Verb Agreement

Practice

Write *am*, *is*, or *are* to agree with the subject in each sentence.

5. We _____**are**_____ learning about plants and trees.

6. A tree _____**is**_____ a wooded plant.

Write *have* or *has* to agree with the subject in each sentence.

7. Evergreens _____**have**_____ leaves or needles.

8. The desert _____**has**_____ many plants.

Proofread

Read the following sentences. Choose the verb in parentheses that correctly completes each sentence.

9. Leaves _____**change**_____ color in the fall. (change, changes)

10. A cactus plant _____**has**_____ spines, but no leaves. (has, have)

GRAMMAR AND USAGE

Transition Words

> **Transition words** help your sentences go together smoothly. Time and order words are examples of transition words.
>
> Here are some transition words:
> first   next   then
> last   later   finally   in the beginning

 **Underline the transition words in each sentence.**

1. I cleared the table. Then, my sister washed the dishes.

2. In the beginning, I liked math class.

3. First, I washed my face.

4. Then, I brushed my teeth.

5. Finally, I brushed my hair.

UNIT 3 Look Again • **Lesson 3** *Hungry Little Hare*

 Transition Words

Practice

Find the transition words in the paragraph. Write them on the lines.

It was time to get ready for the party. I swept the house; meanwhile, Mom put up decorations. Next, we put icing on the cake. Then, Dad made sandwiches. Later, we got the games ready. Finally, we were ready for the party.

meanwhile; Next; Then; Later;

Finally

Comprehension and Language Arts Skills UNIT 3 • Lesson 3 **73**

WRITER'S CRAFT

Name _____ Date _____

Parts of a Sentence

A sentence is a group of words that expresses a complete thought. A sentence has two parts: a naming part and a telling part.

Rule

▸The **subject** of a sentence includes all the words in the naming part.

▸The **predicate** includes all the words in the telling part.

Example

▸   **Subject**

The game of soccer

▸   **Predicate**

is played around the world.

Underline the subject once and underline the predicate twice in each sentence.

1. Soccer began in England in the 1800s.

2. Two teams of 11 players each compete in soccer.

3. The players try to put a ball into the other team's goal.

4. The goals are two nets at opposite ends of a rectangular field.

▶**Parts of a Sentence**

Write an *S* if the underlined part is a subject, and write a *P* if it is a predicate. Put an *S* or *P* on the line after the sentence.

5. The game of rugby uses an oval-shaped ball. **S**

6. The players on a rugby team carry, kick, or pass the ball. **P**

7. Fifteen players make up a team. **P**

8. The object of the game is to score goals. **S**

Read the sentences below. Underline the subject once. Underline the predicate twice.

9. The team with the ball is the offensive team.

10. The game of football developed from the English game of rugby.

11. The team trying to stop the offensive team is the defensive team.

GRAMMAR AND USAGE

Organizing Expository Writing

> ▶ Expository writing gives facts. It tells something true about a subject.
> ▶ Start your expository paragraph with your topic. Then add details. End with a sentence that sums up your main points.
>
> Here are some tips to organize your details:
> ▶ Put the most important facts first.
> ▶ List in the order in which things happen. This can be the events of a day or steps to a recipe.

Number these details in order of importance.

Topic: Doctors

___4___ They go to school for many years.

___2___ They help people feel better.

___1___ They save lives.

___3___ They work in offices and hospitals.

▶ **Organizing Expository Writing**

WRITER'S CRAFT

Write a paragraph based on the facts from this story. Be sure to put the facts in order.

▶ She got a call Saturday afternoon.
▶ Her family put the posters up all over town.
▶ Her dog was found!
▶ Her dog was finally home.
▶ Emma lost her dog.
▶ Her family made posters with her dog's picture and their phone number.

Emma lost her dog. Her family made posters with her dog's picture and their phone number. Her family put the posters up all over town. She got a call Saturday afternoon. Her dog was found! Her dog was finally home.

Supporting Details

> ▶ A **main idea** is the topic of the paragraph.
> ▶ **Supporting details** tell about the main idea.
>
> Main Idea: Farming is hard work.
> Supporting Details:
> ▶ You have to feed the animals.
> ▶ Some farmers plant and harvest.
> ▶ Other farmers milk the cows and do other
>   chores.

Read the main ideas below. Then cross out one sentence that is not a supporting detail.

Main Idea: Moira is in charge of the costumes
                     for the class play.

Details: Moira found some long dresses in
                     her mother's closet.

                     ~~She likes to go to plays.~~

                     She added feathers and buttons to
                     the dresses.

                     They were perfect for the ballroom
                     scene in the play at school.

Supporting Details

Write three supporting details about the topic below.

Topic: Weekends are fun.

Answers will vary.

_____

_____

_____

WRITER'S CRAFT

Name _____ Date _____

Classify and Categorize

Focus **Classifying and categorizing** means putting things into groups. Classifying can help readers keep track of information in a story.

> To classify information
> ▶ name the categories for things, characters, or events
> ▶ list the things, characters, or events that fit under each category
> ▶ sometimes things, characters, or events can fit into more than one category

 **Identify**

The characters in "How the Guinea Fowl Got Her Spots" can be classified in a number of different ways. Look at the categories listed below and write the animals that fit under each.

Friends: ___Guinea Fowl and Cow___

Large animals: ___Cow, Lion___

Small animals: ___Guinea Fowl___

Four-legged animals: ___Cow, Lion___

UNIT 3 Look Again • **Lesson 5** *How the Guinea Fowl Got Her Spots*

▶ Classify and Categorize

Practice

Look at the list of things below. List each thing under the correct category. Remember, some things can fit in more than one category.

| cutting board | scissors | board |
| sponge | eraser | paper | can opener |

Things that are useful in a school classroom

scissors

board

eraser

paper

Things that are useful in a kitchen

cutting board

scissors

sponge

can opener

Apply

Make a list of other things that would fit into each of the categories.

School classroom: **Answers will vary.**

_____

Kitchen: _____

_____

COMPREHENSION

Name _____ Date _____

UNIT 3 Look Again • **Lesson 5** *How the Guinea Fowl Got Her Spots*

Complete Sentences

A **complete sentence** has a subject and a predicate.
A **run-on sentence** is two ideas mixed together.
A **sentence fragment** is missing a subject or predicate.

Rule	**Example**
	Run-on
▶ To correct a run-on sentence, write two sentences.	▶ The fog covers the bridge it stands over the water.
	Correct
	The fog covers the bridge. It stands over the water.
	Fragment
▶ To correct a sentence fragment, add the missing subject or predicate to the sentence.	▶ Over one billion vehicles
	Correct
	Over one billion vehicles have crossed the bridge.

Write *F* for fragment or *R* for run-on.

1. Orange trees plenty of water. __F__

2. Potatoes grow in cool climates they can't

   grow in freezing weather. __R__

82 UNIT 3 • Lesson 5   Comprehension and Language Arts Skills

▶ Complete Sentences

Circle the word group that correctly completes each sentence.

3. The first bridges (were tree trunks.) some footbridges.

4. Pontoon bridges   the surface. (float on the water.)

5. Arches   (are very strong.) curved supports.

Read the paragraph below. Correct the run-on sentences. Write in end marks and underline three (≡) times the letters that should be capitalized.

A map has arrows that show directions⊙the main directions are north, south, east, and west. There are also directions between the four main directions. The direction between north and east is called northeast⊙southeast is between south and east. Between west and north is called northwest, and between west and south is called southwest.

Place and Location Words

> ▶ Place and location words tell where something is.
>
> Some place and location words are:
>
> | | | | |
> |---|---|---|---|
> | above | over | in front of | next to |
> | on top of | below | beneath | under |
> | near | inside | outside | beside |

 **Look around your classroom and answer these questions. Use place and location words from the box.**

1. Where is your teacher's desk?

Answers will vary.

2. Where is the pencil sharpener?

Answers will vary.

3. Where are your books?

Answers will vary.

4. Where is your coat?

Answers will vary.

▶ **Place and Location Words**

Finish these sentences about things in
your bedroom.

5. __**Answers will vary.**_____ is on top of
the bed.

6. __**Answers will vary.**_____ is beneath
the bed.

7. __**Answers will vary.**_____ is beside
the bed.

8. __**Answers will vary.**_____ is on top of
the dresser.

9. __**Answers will vary.**_____ is in front
of the dresser.

WRITER'S CRAFT

Main Idea

Focus   The **main idea** tells what a paragraph is mostly about.

> ▶ A **main-idea sentence** gives the main idea of a paragraph. The other sentences in a paragraph give details or information about the main idea.
>
> ▶ A main-idea sentence often comes **first** in a paragraph. Placing the main idea sentence first helps readers know what the paragraph is about.

Identify

Look through "Animal Camouflage" for main-idea sentences. Write one main-idea sentence below. Then give some details about the main idea.

Answers will vary.

Page: _____

Main idea: _____

_____

Details about the main idea: _____

_____

_____

▶ **Main Idea**

Read the paragraph. It is missing a main-idea sentence. Choose the best main-idea sentence from the box and write it on the lines.

Parents tell their children stories about their childhoods. Grandparents talk about their lives and their parents' lives. When we learn our family's stories, we can tell our children the stories too.

> Storytellers entertain many people.
> Families have picnics together.
> Stories help bring families together.

Stories help bring families together.

_____

Add your own sentence to the paragraph above. It should give more information about the main idea.

Sentences will vary.

_____

COMPREHENSION

Review

▶ Kinds of Sentences

Read the sentences below. Add the correct end mark.

1. The colors of the tree frog tell others to beware**.**

2. Do bees like flowers**?**

3. I love going to the park**!**

▶ Linking and Helping Verbs

Underline the linking verbs and circle the helping verbs in the sentences below.

4. A deer (was) running in the forest.

5. His antlers <u>were</u> big.

6. A female deer <u>is</u> a doe.

▶ Subject-Verb Agreement

Read the sentences below. Fill in the correct word.

7. I ___like___ to write letters. (like/likes)

8. My friends ___give___ me letters all the time. (give/gives)

GRAMMAR AND USAGE

▶ Parts of a Sentence

Underline the subject once and underline the predicate twice.

9. Pumas are members of the cat family.

10. A puma can live in a hot area or in a forest.

11. The mountain lion is another name for the puma.

12. Pumas have sharp teeth.

13. A puma's speed helps it stay alive.

▶ Complete Sentences

Write *F* for fragment, *R* for run-on, or *C* for complete sentence after each of the following groups of words.

14. White light contains all the colors of the rainbow. __C__

15. A flower's colors bees. __F__

16. Squirrels are color-blind guinea pigs are, too. __R__

17. Red shoes in blue light. __F__

Fact and Opinion

A **fact** can be checked and proven to be true.
An **opinion** cannot be proven. It is a person's idea or feeling.

▶ Fact: Germany is in Europe.
▶ Opinion: Germany is a nice place to visit.

Read each sentence. Write *F* for fact or *O* for opinion.

1. __O__ My mother is the best lawyer in the world.

2. __F__ Tomorrow we have gym in the afternoon.

3. __F__ Mushrooms grow in the ground.

4. __O__ My friend has the nicest bike.

5. __F__ Trenton is the capital of New Jersey.

UNIT 3 Look Again • **Lesson 6** *Animal Camouflage*

▶**Fact and Opinion**

Practice

Read the following facts. Then change the fact to an opinion. The first one is done for you.

6. Fact: There are many breeds of rabbits.

Opinion: White rabbits are the best breed.

7. Fact: There are fifty states in the United States.

Opinion: **Answers will vary.**

8. Fact: Marshmallows are made with sugar.

Opinion: **Answers will vary.**

9. Fact: Trees give off oxygen.

Opinion: **Answers will vary.**

10. Fact: Florida has many beaches.

Opinion: **Answers will vary.**

WRITER'S CRAFT

Adjectives

Adjectives make writing more interesting. Forming a picture in your mind of the objects you want to describe will help you find the right adjectives.

Rule	**Example**
▶ An **adjective** is a word that describes a noun. An adjective tells *how much*, *how many*, or *what kind*.	▶ There are **five** classes of **living** things.
▶ **Articles** are special kinds of adjectives. There are three articles: *a*, *an*, and *the*.	▶ **An** insect or **a** bird might be included in **the** animal class.

Read the poem below. Circle the adjectives and articles.

For (a) (big) (green) plant
Or (a) (tiny) (little) ant
Resting in (the) woods is nice.
Each (living) thing must
Share (cool) shade and just
Take (a) break in paradise.

Adjectives

Practice

Circle the adjectives and underline the articles in the sentences below.

1. The (black) bat and the (blue) whale are mammals.

2. (Big) elephants and (little) rats are mammals too.

3. (All) mammals have (thick) fur.

4. (Tall) giraffes and (short) monkeys have fur.

5. What mammals have (brown) fur?

Proofread

Read the paragraph below. Underline the articles and circle the adjectives.

Many creatures live in the forest. (Blue) peacocks and (brown) owls live in forests. (Red) deer and (gray) squirrels live there, too. (Green) frogs live in forests that are near water. Sometimes, a (white) rabbit can be found hopping through the forest. How many bears have you seen in the forest? I saw (two) bears last year!

GRAMMAR AND USAGE

Fact and Opinion

Focus Writers use facts and opinions to support ideas in their writing.

> ▶ A **fact** is a statement that can be proven true.
> ▶ An **opinion** is what someone feels or believes is true. Opinions cannot be proven true or false.

Look at the statements about "The Dinosaur Who Lived In My Backyard." In the spaces next to each statement, write *fact* if the statement is a fact. Write *opinion* if it is an opinion.

1. Dinosaurs hatched from eggs. __fact__

2. The dinosaur in this story ate only vegetables. __fact__

3. The boy's mother believed that if you eat all

your vegetables you'll grow very strong. __opinion__

4. The boy's town was a swamp a long time ago. __fact__

5. Dinosaurs lived a long time ago. __fact__

6. The boy believed that it would be pretty hard to keep a

dinosaur happy. __opinion__

►Fact and Opinion

COMPREHENSION

Add a fact or an opinion to each sentence below. Use the clues in parentheses.

7. (opinion) Babies like to  **Answers will vary.** _____

_____

8. (fact) A globe shows _____

_____

Apply

Based on what you learned from "The Dinosaur Who Lived in My Backyard" and "Fossils Tell of Long Ago," write one sentence about dinosaurs that is a fact and one that is an opinion.

9. **Answers will vary.** _____

_____

10. _____

_____

UNIT 4 Fossils • **Lesson 2** *The Dinosaur Who Lived in My Backyard*

Contractions

Contractions make writing sound more like a
conversation. There are two kinds of contractions.

Rule	Example
▶ A **contraction** may be formed by putting together a verb and the word *not*.	▶ are not—aren't could not—couldn't did not—didn't do not—don't has not—hasn't was not—wasn't
▶ A **contraction** may be formed by combining a pronoun and a verb.	▶ I am—I'm who is—who's it is, it has—it's

**Circle the correct contraction in each
sentence below.**

1. Greenland (isn't) **don't** a continent.

2. There **won't** (aren't) a lot of people
   living in Greenland.

3. Hawaii (wasn't) **weren't** a state until
   1959.

▶ **Contractions**

GRAMMAR AND USAGE

Write the contraction for the boldfaced words in each sentence below.

4. **I am** going to Arizona in April. _____ I'm _____

5. **I have** never been to the Southwest. _____ I've _____

6. **I will** send you a postcard of the desert. _____ I'll _____

7. **She is** my best friend. _____ She's _____

8. I know **he is** coming to visit today. _____ he's _____

Add apostrophes where needed to make contractions. Use proofreading marks.

   I couldn't think of anything to write. We're supposed to write a poem for class. It doesn't have to be a long poem. I can't think tonight! Couldn't I write about my life? I could, if it weren't so late.

Poetry joins the sounds and meanings of words to create ideas and feelings.

Rule	**Example**
▶ In **rhyming** poetry, the last word in a line rhymes with the last word in another line.	▶ Hickory dickory **dock** The mouse ran up the **clock.**

 **Underline the rhyming words in each line.**

Bill and Ted went to the <u>park</u>.
While there, they heard a dog <u>bark</u>.

They looked around and could not find <u>it</u>
But they did not want to <u>quit</u>.

They looked behind the swings and under the <u>slide</u>
To see where they thought a dog might <u>hide</u>.

They finally found him behind a <u>tree</u>
Just as happy as can <u>be</u>.

▶ Rhyme

 **Practice**

Write a poem about your favorite toy. Be sure to use rhyming words in your poem.

Answers will vary.

_____

_____

_____

_____

WRITER'S CRAFT

Classify and Categorize

Focus A writer often includes many details in a story. **Classifying or categorizing** the information can help show how details are related.

> Readers sort information into different groups, or **categories.** This helps them understand and remember what they read.

Identify

Look at the illustration on pages 56–57 in "Dinosaur Fossils." Use the illustration to sort the information into the two categories.

Name of dinosaur	**Where it lived**
Tyrannosaurus	North America
Stenonychosaurus	North America
Saltasaurus	South America
Iguanodon	Europe
Velociraptor	Asia
Vulcanodon	Africa

Comprehension and Language Arts Skills

▶**Classify and Categorize**

COMPREHENSION

Make a list for each category below.

Things I like to do　　**Things I don't like to do**

Answers will vary.　　_____

_____　　_____

_____　　_____

_____　　_____

Apply

Look at each item below. Think of two categories to sort these items into and write them in the box. Then sort the items under the two categories.

| subways   tractors   barns   skyscrapers |
| fields   many people |

| **Things in a city** | **Things on a farm** |

subways _____ 　barns _____

many people _____ 　tractors _____

skyscrapers _____ 　fields _____

Linking and Helping Verb Tenses

Finding the right verb and using the right tense of the verb is important in both speaking and writing. You can make your writing better by using the proper tense.

Rule	**Example**
▶A **present tense** linking or helping verb tells about something that is happening now.	▶The Nile River **is** the longest river in the world.
▶A **past tense** linking or helping verb tells about something that happened in the past.	▶The Nile River **was** important to the people in Egypt.

 **Try It!**

Underline the past tense verbs.

1. Louis Braille <u>was</u> a teacher.

2. He <u>was</u> blinded at the age of three.

3. In school, he <u>could</u> not read or write.

4. Then, he <u>was</u> sent to a school in Paris.

UNIT 4 Fossils • **Lesson 3** *Dinosaur Fossils*

Linking and Helping Verb Tenses

Practice

Write the correct verb in the space in each sentence.

5. France ___**is**___ a country in Europe.

6. The area ___**was**___ ruled by the Romans.

7. We ___**are**___ studying French history.

8. Yesterday we ___**were**___ singing songs.

9. Today we ___**are**___ painting pictures.

Proofread

Read the sentences below and find the mistakes. Cross out the incorrect verb and write the correct one above it.

Once I was riding a horse in a desert. My

horse ~~am~~ *was* running very fast. We ~~is~~ *were* trying to

reach a town. The town ~~are~~ *was* very far away.

When the moon ~~have~~ *had* risen in the sky, we saw

the friendly town! The people there ~~was~~ *were* very

friendly.

GRAMMAR AND USAGE

UNIT 4 Fossils • **Lesson 3** *Dinosaur Fossils*

Figurative Language

Figurative language is a word or group of words that stand for more than their real meanings. They are used to create pictures in a reader's mind.

Figures of Speech

▶ A **simile** compares two things by using the word *like* or *as*.

▶ A **metaphor** compares two things without using the word *like* or *as*.

▶ **Personification** gives an object human qualities.

▶ The rabbit's fur was **like** a blanket of soft snow.

▶ The rabbit's fur **was** a blanket of soft snow.

▶ The car **coughed** and **wheezed** as it tried to start.

After each sentence, write *S* if it has a simile, *M* if it has a metaphor, and *P* if it has personification.

1. Adam's eyes were big saucers. ___M___

2. Susan fell like a rock. ___S___

3. The kite was a bird flying in the sky. ___M___

4. The tree danced in the wind. ___P___

5. His bag was as heavy as a brick. ___S___

Name _____ Date _____

► **Figurative Language**

Practice

Compare these things by writing a word to finish each sentence.

1. The cereal tasted like _Answers will vary._____

2. I ran as fast as _Answers will vary._____

3. The banana felt like _Answers will vary._____

4. These shoes are as big as _Answers will vary._____

5. The kitchen smells like _Answers will vary._____

WRITER'S CRAFT

Nouns: Singular and Plural

Nouns can be **singular** or **plural**.

Rule	Example
▶A singular noun names one.	▶star animal plant idea
▶Plural nouns name more than one.	▶stars animals plants ideas
▶Most nouns add -*s* to form the plural form.	▶cars bikes trains
▶Some nouns add -*es* to words ending in *s*, *x*, *z*, *ss*, *ch*, or *sh*.	▶brush brushes box boxes
▶Other nouns ending in *y* change the *y* to -*i* and add -*es*.	▶buddy buddies
▶There are some special nouns. These nouns change when they are made plural.	▶wolf wolves

Try It!

Circle the plural nouns and underline the singular nouns in the sentences below.

1. Some (parts) of the world are always hot.

2. At the equator, (climates) are hot and rainy.

UNIT 4 Fossils • **Lesson 4** *Why Did the Dinosaurs Disappear?*

▶ Nouns: Singular and Plural

Practice

Write the plural form of each noun below.

3. ax _____ axes

4. rocket _____ rockets

5. hat _____ hats

6. man _____ men

7. sky _____ skies

Proofread

Find the mistakes in the paragraph below. Cross out the incorrect word, and write the correct form of the word above it.

One-fifth of Earth is covered with deserts.
Deserts have only a few plantes and animales.

plants   animals

No cloudes can form in deserts, because there

clouds

is not much rain. There are a lot of sand dunes.
Cameles and snakees can live in deserts also.

Camels   snakes

UNIT 4 Fossils • **Lesson 4** *Why Did the Dinosaurs Disappear?*

Organizing Descriptive Writing

> ▶ **Descriptions** are words that make a picture in the reader's mind.
>
> ▶ Start your descriptive paragraph with your topic. Then add details that make a picture in the reader's mind. End with a sentence that sums up your main points.

Try It! **Write a descriptive sentence about each topic. Be sure to use describing words.**

1. Topic: Your best friend

Answers will vary. _____

2. Topic: Your pet or favorite animal

Answers will vary. _____

3. Topic: Your school

Answers will vary. _____

UNIT 4 Fossils • **Lesson 4** *Why Did the Dinosaurs Disappear?*

▶ Organizing Descriptive Writing

Practice

Write a paragraph describing your house. Write details about how things look, feel, smell, and sound.

Answers will vary. _____

_____

_____

_____

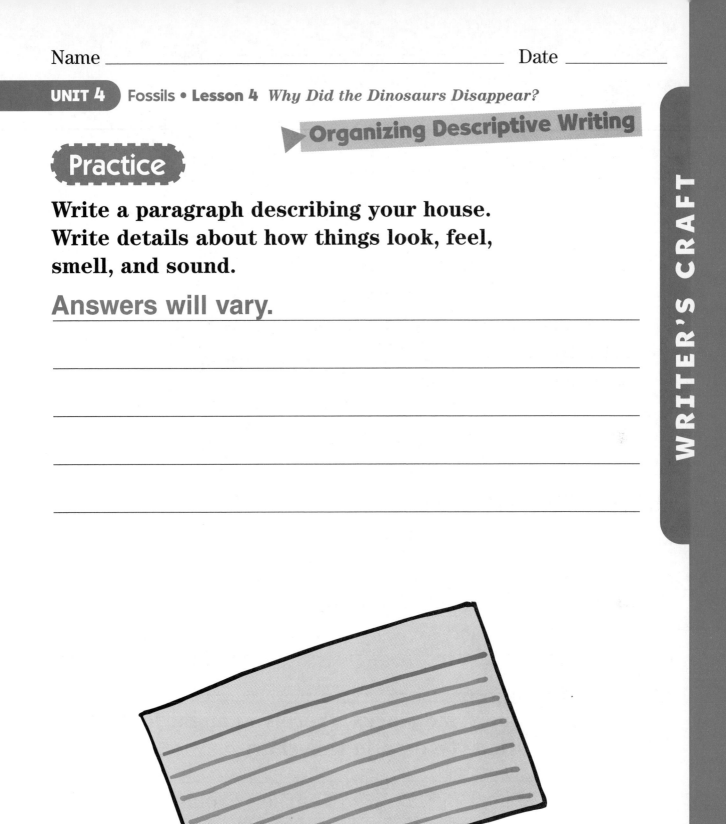

Collecting and Organizing Data

Data is information about something. There are many places to collect data. You have to know where to look. Some places to find information:

▶ An **atlas** is a book of maps.

▶ A **dictionary** lists words in ABC order. You can find a word's spelling and meaning.

▶ An **encyclopedia** has facts on many subjects.

▶ **Magazines** and **newspapers** have many up-to-date facts.

▶ You can also get information from a **museum** or **zoo.**

Organize data in a way that makes sense.

Ways to organize your data:

▶ A **chart** is a box that has rows and columns. Words are written in boxes to help readers find information quickly.

▶ A **time line** shows the order in which events happen over a period of time.

 **Name some places where you might look to find the data in this chart.**

Animal	Male	Female	Young
Chicken	Rooster	Hen	Chick
Rabbit	Buck	Doe	Bunny
Whale	Bull	Cow	Calf

Encyclopedia, book about animals, zoo

▶ **Collecting and Organizing Data**

Practice

Tell where you might find data about these topics.

1. Places in South Africa — *atlas*

2. The latest news — *newspaper or magazine*

3. The meanings of words — *dictionary*

4. Jupiter — *encyclopedia*

5. Dinosaurs — *encyclopedia or museum*

WRITER'S CRAFT

Sequence

Focus Sequence is the order of what happens in a story. Writers often use **time and order words** to help readers follow the sequence.

> **Time and order** words show
>
> ▶ the **order** in which events happen. Words such as *first, then, so, when,* and *finally* show order.
>
> ▶ the passage of **time** in a story. Words such as *winter, today,* and *night* show time.

Identify

Look through "Monster Tracks." Find sentences with time and order words. Write the page numbers and the words. Write *T* next to the word if it shows time and *O* if it shows order.

Answers will vary. Possible answers are shown.

1. Page: 83   Word: First—O

2. Page: 85   Word: then—O

3. Page: 87   Word: first—O

4. Page: 87   Word: Then—O

5. Page: 88   Word: fifteen minutes—T

Sequence

COMPREHENSION

Practice

Read the paragraph below. Fill in the spaces
with words that show time.   **Answers will vary.**
Possible answers are
____On Saturday____ my sister and I made dinner   **shown.**

for our friends. We invited them to come over

____last week____ . ____Next week____ we are

going to invite our cousins, too.

In the paragraph below, fill in the spaces with
words that show order.

The ____first____ step in making scrambled
eggs is to mix eggs with milk, salt, and pepper.

____Before____ pouring the eggs in the pan,

melt butter in the pan. ____Next____ pour
the eggs and milk into the pan.

____Then____ cook 3 to 4 minutes.

Apply

Write two sentences about what you did yesterday.
Use time and order words.

Answers will vary. _____

_____

Adverbs

> **Adverbs** make writing more clear and more descriptive. You can make your verbs stronger with adverbs.
>
> | **Rule** | **Example** |
> |---|---|
> | ▶ An adverb describes a verb and tells *how, when,* or *where*. | ▶ The bones in your body grow **fast.** I went to the store **yesterday.** Stay **here** and drink your milk. |

Read the sentences. Circle the adverbs.

1. Your muscles let you move (easily.)

2. Cardiac muscle keeps your heart beating (strongly.)

3. Skeletal muscles let us move our bones (slowly.)

4. You can (usually) control your skeletal muscles.

5. Nerve signals from the brain (always) tell the muscles what to do.

UNIT 4 Fossils • **Lesson 5** *Monster Tracks*

▶ **Adverbs**

Read the sentences below. Write an adverb
in the blank that best completes the
sentence.

6. The cheetah can run _____quickly_____.

7. They ____sometimes____ stretch their arms
and legs.

8. Some cheetahs swim _____well_____.

9. A cheetah can growl _____loudly_____.

10. Baby cheetahs _____always_____ stay close
to their mothers.

Proofread

Read the paragraph below. Circle the
adverbs.

Ants and termites live in large colonies. Ants
have long legs and can run (swiftly.) They can
climb (anywhere.) Termites eat (mostly) plants.
Many termites build mounds underground. The
mounds have thick walls to keep out anteaters.
Ants can (easily) lift things that weigh more than
they do. Army ants are (always) on the move. The
queen waits (patiently) for the workers to bring
her food. Studying insects is (sometimes) fun.

GRAMMAR AND USAGE

Paragraph Form

Rules for Writing Paragraphs:

1. Begin a paragraph on a new line.
2. Indent the first line of each paragraph.
3. Write a topic sentence at the beginning of the paragraph that tells the main idea.
4. Write sentences that support the main idea.
5. Begin a new paragraph for each new idea.

Try It! **Tell what is missing from this paragraph.**

There are over 400 species of them. They live in the ocean. Their fins and tails help them to swim fast. They eat other, smaller fish. The great white is the largest type of shark. It is about 15 feet long. Sharks are interesting fish.

indent; topic sentence

_____

▶**Paragraph Form**

Practice

Write a paragraph telling about your favorite holiday. Make sure you include all the parts in your paragraph.

Answers will vary.

_____

_____

_____

_____

WRITER'S CRAFT

Review

Adjectives and Adverbs

Read the sentences below. Circle the adjectives and underline the adverbs in each sentence.

1. Gems are stones used to make (pretty) jewelry.

2. Gemstones are <u>often</u> found at the bottom of rivers.

3. Diamond is a (hard) material.

Contractions

Form contractions from the boldfaced words in each sentence.

4. Rocks on Earth's surface **do not** last forever. **don't**

5. They **cannot** withstand the effects of rain and wind. **can't**

6. These rocks **are not** very old. **aren't**

7. You **would not** want to eat those minerals. **wouldn't**

▶ **Review**

GRAMMAR AND USAGE

▶ Linking and Helping Verb Tenses

Look at the words in boldface. Write a *pr* if the verb is present tense and a *pt* if the verb is past tense.

8. These mountains **were formed** in the Ice Age. _pt_

9. These pies **are** not pumpkin. _pr_

10. This picture **was taken** 50 years ago. _pt_

11. My grandmother **was** 50 last year. _pt_

12. Who **is helping** with the decorations? _pr_

▶ Nouns: Singular and Plural

Write the plural or singular form of the boldfaced noun on the line at the end of each sentence.

13. The lioness has one **baby**. _babies_

14. Autumn is the time to rake all the **leaves** in the yard. _leaf_

15. The **boys** are better at yard work. _boy_

16. Does your city have more than one **library**? _libraries_

17. Please put this book back on the **shelf**. _shelves_

Topic Sentences

Rule	Example
▶ A topic sentence tells the main idea of the paragraph. It is often the first sentence of a paragraph.	▶ **Topic Sentence:** Painting is fun. This sentence tells the reader the paragraph is about painting.

Try It!   **Circle the topic sentence.**

1. It is the highest mountain in Japan.

2. The view from the top is amazing.

3. It is 12,388 feet tall.

4. (Mt. Fuji is Japan's most popular place to visit.)

5. It is a breathtaking sight.

▶**Topic Sentences**

 **Practice**

Write a topic sentence for this paragraph.

It is a brass instrument that is hollow inside. It makes sounds when air is blown into the cup-shaped mouthpiece. It has a fancy design. The French horn has been around for many years.

Answers will vary.

_____

_____

Write a topic sentence about your favorite instrument.

Answers will vary.

_____

_____

WRITER'S CRAFT

Point of View

Focus **Point of view** is how the author decides to tell the story. He or she can tell it through a character or through someone outside of the story.

When a story is told from the **first-person point of view**
▶ the storyteller is a character in the story
▶ the clue words *I, my, mine, us, our*, and *we* are used

When a story is told from the **third-person point of view**
▶ the storyteller is not a character in the story
▶ the clue words *she, he, her, they*, and *their* are used

 Identify

Read page 123 of "Molly the Brave and Me" for clue words that show who is telling the story. Write the clue words and the name of the character telling the story.

Clue words: **Answers will vary.**

Who is telling the story? **Beth**

▶ **Point of View**

Find an example in which the storyteller shares her own thoughts or feelings. Write the first three or four words of the example. Share your example with your classmates.

Page: _____ Example: _____

_____

Circle each word that gives a clue about the point of view.

1. Marsha and (her) mother almost missed the plane. (They) had a hard time getting a taxi to the airport. Luckily, (their) plane was late taking off.

2. Jamie and (I) shared (our) snacks. Dad gave (us) apples, sandwiches, and peanuts. (We) ate the snacks at the picnic table.

Write about something you and a friend did together. Write using first-person point of view.

Sentences will vary.

_____

_____

COMPREHENSION

Capitalization: I and Proper Nouns

There are many places to use capital letters. Use them in proper nouns.

Rule	**Example**
▶ The word *I* is always written as a capital letter.	▶ My brother and **I** took a boat trip down the river.
▶ A proper noun names a particular person, place, or thing. A proper noun always begins with a capital letter.	▶ The **Nile River** is longer than the **Tigris River.**

 **Try It!**

Read the sentences below. Circle the proper nouns in the sentences below that should be capitalized.

1. The third president of the (united) (states) was (thomas) (jefferson.)

2. Jefferson was born in (virginia.)

3. In 1776, (jefferson) wrote the (declaration) of (independence.)

▶**Capitalization: I and Proper Nouns**

Practice

Circle the word with the correct capital letters.

4. (Maria) **maria** and I are going to study Lewis and Clark.

5. We learned that they went west of the **missouri river** (Missouri River.)

6. **i** (I) read that they reached the Pacific Ocean.

7. Sacajawea was a (Native American) **native american** that guided the explorers.

Proofread

Underline three times (≡) each letter in the paragraph below that should be a capital letter.

Last saturday, i saw a white tiger at the San Diego Zoo. He sat alone as my uncle john and i watched him. The african Safari area is my favorite place. The big gorilla named bob is always funny to see.

MECHANICS

Organizing Narrative Writing

> ▶ **Narrative writing** tells a story.
>
> ▶ Narrative writing has three parts: Characters, Plot, and Setting.
>
> ▶ A narrative can be a real story, like something that happened to you or a friend.
>
> ▶ A narrative can also be a made-up story, like a fairy tale.
>
> ▶ Always try to have an exciting beginning and ending.

Think of a story that you would like to tell. List the characters on the lines.

Characters

Answers will vary. _____

_____

_____

Name _____ Date _____

Organizing Narrative Writing

Practice

Think about your story. Write a sentence or two describing your plot.

<u>Plot</u>

Answers will vary.

_____

_____

_____

Where is your story going to take place? Write a list of adjectives that describe your story's setting.

<u>Setting</u>

Answers will vary.

_____

_____

_____

WRITER'S CRAFT

UNIT 5 Courage • **Lesson 2** *Dragons and Giants*

Conjunctions and Interjections

Conjunctions and **interjections** are special words. Use them to make writing easier or more interesting to read.

Rule	**Example**
▶ A **conjunction** is a word that connects words or ideas.	▶ Ziggy **and** I are going to the zoo. We will go today **or** tomorrow.
▶ An **interjection** is a word that shows strong feelings. It is followed by an exclamation point.	▶ **Yes!** I would love to come to your party. **No!** I won't bring my little brother.

Read the sentences. Circle the conjunctions. Underline the interjections.

1. My sister read a story to my brother (and) me.

2. <u>Oh!</u> Alice just fell down into a big hole.

3. She was following a rabbit, (or) was it a hare?

4. <u>Goodness!</u> She fell down (and) hurt her knee.

Name _____ Date _____

▶ Conjunctions and Interjections

Read the sentences. Write *and, or,* or *but* to complete each sentence.

5. Mom ___and___ I are going to walk to school by ourselves today.

6. We will walk, ___or___ we may run.

7. We may even skip, ___but___ we won't be late for school.

8. Mom is wearing a blue coat ___and___ a green hat.

9. I am wearing a red jacket, ___and___ I am wearing a red cap today.

Proofread

Read the following story. Add an exclamation mark after the interjections.

The sidewalks and the streets were slippery with snow. Oh, no!How would I get to school safely today? I bundled myself up in my coat and my hat. Oops!I almost forgot my gloves. Now I'm finally ready to go. The steps at school are spread with salt.Wow!This is easy.

MECHANICS

Plot

A story's **plot** is made up of the things that happen in the story.

▶ A plot has a beginning, middle, and end.

▶ The characters have a problem. The problem is solved at the end of the story.

▶ Usually ends with a climax, or high point, of the story and a solution to the problem.

Look at the story "Dragons and Giants." Look for the main characters, plot, and setting. List below.

Characters: <u>Frog and Toad</u>

_____

Setting: <u>outside</u>

_____

Problem: <u>scared of things outside</u>

_____

Plot

Write about the story "Dragons and Giants." Be sure to tell about the plot.

Answers will vary.

WRITER'S CRAFT

Suspense and Surprise

> ▶ **Suspense** makes the reader want to find out what happens next.
> ▶ **Surprise** is when something happens that the reader didn't expect.

Read each paragraph. Circle the letter of the paragraph that has suspense.

A. It was a rainy, windy night. There was a loud noise at the door. I opened the door. There was no one there. My dog came out from behind the steps. He was all wet and shaking. He had scared me. I'd forgotten I had left him outside.

B. It was a dark and stormy night. Suddenly, I heard a strange noise. It came from the front door. Again and again, I heard the same sound. What could make such a sound? I had to know. I took a deep breath and flung open the door. I jumped! As I breathed a sigh of relief, my dog came out from behind the steps. He was trembling and soaked. I had left him out in the rain!

Suspense and Surprise

Write a paragraph about an ordinary afternoon in your school's library. Plan a surprise ending.

Answers will vary. _____

_____

_____

_____

WRITER'S CRAFT

Cause and Effect

Focus **Cause** and **effect** is when one thing causes another thing to happen.

> ▶The **cause** is why something happens.
> ▶The **effect** is what happens.

Look in "A Hole in the Dike" for the effects listed below. Then write the cause for each.

1. Effect: Peter got off his bike to see what was wrong.

Cause: __Suddenly he heard a soft, gurgling noise.__

__He saw a small stream of water trickling through a__

__small hole in the dike below.__

2. Effect: All the people thanked Peter. They carried him on their shoulders, shouting, "Make way for the hero of Holland! The brave boy who saved our land!"

Cause: __All night long Peter kept his finger in the dike.__

__His fingers grew cold and numb. He wanted to sleep,__

__but he couldn't give up.__

UNIT 5 Courage • **Lesson 3** *A Hole in the Dike*

▶**Cause and Effect**

Read each sentence. Write the effect (what happened) and the cause (why it happened).

3. Because it was hot, my friends went swimming.

Effect: **My friends went swimming.**

Cause: **It was hot.**

4. Since we wanted to be helpful, we picked up our toys.

Effect: **We picked up our toys.**

Cause: **We wanted to be helpful.**

Apply

Write a sentence of your own that shows a cause and an effect. Draw a line under the cause in your sentence.

Answers will vary.

_____

_____

COMPREHENSION

Commas in Dialogue

There are many places to use commas. One place is in dialogue.

Rule

▶ A comma is used before the quotation marks that begin a speaker's exact words.

▶ A comma is used after the word before the end quotes.

Example

▶ I said to my dog, "Jump over this log."

▶ "I want to watch him jump," said my friend Mai.

Read the sentences. Put commas where they belong.

1. Joe said ,"I need to buy some carrots."

2. Charlotte sighed ,"Tomorrow is another day."

3. "I cannot sell my cat", I said.

4. I added ,"I will give her to you as a present."

5. I said ,"I want to visit her each Saturday."

Commas in Dialogue

 **Practice**

Write a comma where it is needed in each sentence.

6. Misha said,"I don't think this is a treasure map."

7. Sasha replied,"Oh, yes it is."

8. Trisha sighed,"Some diamonds would be nice."

9. Misha said,"Maybe we'll find gold!"

10. "Just some money would suit me fine," said Sasha.

Proofread

Read the story. Write commas where they are missing in the sentences with dialogue. Use proofreading marks.

   Once upon a time there were three sisters. Each sister had a cat. One day, a sister said,"I would like to have another cat." So the family went to the cat shelter downtown and found a stray cat to take home. The youngest sister said,"I am glad we are able to give another cat a home."

MECHANICS

Characterization

> **Characterization** is the writer's way of showing what the characters in a story are like. Writers do this by telling what the characters do, say, think, and feel.

Read each sentence. Decide what the author is trying to show the reader. Write *acts*, *says*, *thinks*, or *feels* on the line.

1. Dan sighed with regret. ___acts___

2. She thought it was her fault. ___thinks___

3. "I can't wait to go home!" said Shelly.

___says___

4. She was sick with worry. ___feels___

UNIT 5 Courage • **Lesson 3** *A Hole in the Dike*

▶ **Characterization**

Read the paragraph. Then write the answers to each question.

Tony had to give a report at school. "I don't like speaking in front of the class," Tony said to his mother. Later, Mrs. O'Brien announced, "The next report is by Tony Perez." Tony walked to the front of the class. He began his report. He thought his voice was too loud. He felt his knees shake.

1. How did Tony feel about speaking in front of his class before his report?

He didn't like it.

2. What did Tony say about speaking in front of his class?

"I don't like speaking in front of the class."

3. How did he act when he began his report?

He was nervous; his knees were shaking.

WRITER'S CRAFT

Setting

The **setting** of a story is the time and place in which the story happens.
Settings:
▶ A high school in the morning
▶ Maine in the fall
▶ A book store in 1962

For each topic, tell when and where the story might take place.

1. Topic: A bike ride   **Answers will vary.**

2. Topic: A concert   **Answers will vary.**

3. Topic: A party   **Answers will vary.**

UNIT 5 Courage • **Lesson 3** *A Hole in the Dike*

▶ **Setting**

Read the story and answer the questions. Then tell about the setting in your own words.

Our scout troop went for a hike in a forest last summer. The trees were so thick that it was dark, even in the morning! Not one ray of sunlight could get through the trees. Sometimes we couldn't see the trail. We had to follow the forest ranger. The ranger taught us lots of things about the forest. I think I may become a forest ranger.

4. When did this story take place?

last summer

5. Where did this story take place?

in a forest

6. Tell about the setting in your own words.

Answers will vary but should describe a dark place with many trees.

WRITER'S CRAFT

UNIT 5 Courage • **Lesson 4** *Martin Luther King, Jr.*

Capitalization: Titles and Initials

There are many places to use capital letters. Use capital letters in titles and initials.

Rule	**Example**
▶ Titles in people's names begin with capital letters.	▶ **Mr.** Tilly told us to form a straight line. **Dr.** Jilly gave me a checkup today.
▶ Initials from people's names are capitalized.	▶ **E. B.** White is the author of *Stuart Little*.

Try It!

Underline three times (≡) each title or set of initials that should be capitalized in the sentences below.

1. John Adams and John q. Adams were both presidents of the United States.

2. The president of the United States is called mr. President.

3. Presidents t. Roosevelt and Franklin d. Roosevelt were cousins.

▶ **Capitalization: Titles and Initials**

MECHANICS

Practice

Write an initial or title in the blank.

4. Our family doctor is ___Dr.___ Laurel.

5. The soccer coach at our school is ___Mr./Miss/Mrs.___ Wang-Lui.

6. The gorilla at the zoo was named ___Mr./Miss/Mrs.___ Big.

7. The veterinarian who takes care of our cats is named ___Dr.___ Tawney.

8. Did you ever see Jeff's dad, ___Mr.___ Cole?

Proofread

Read the story below. Underline three times (≡) all the titles of people and all the initials that should be capitalized. Use proofreading marks.

　　The architect i. m. Pei was born in China in 1917. mr. Pei has designed many large, beautiful buildings. In 1960, he designed the terminal at jfk International Airport in New York. A landscape architect designs gardens and outdoor spaces. The first person to call himself a landscape architect was f. l. Olmsted.

Dialogue

Dialogue tells the reader exactly what the characters say.

Rules	**Example**
Rules for showing what characters are saying:	▶ Ken said, "Let's go to the mall."
▶ Put quotation marks (" ") before and after a speaker's exact words.	"That's a great idea," said Pam.
▶ Always begin the first word of a quotation with a capital letter.	
▶ Use a comma to separate a quote from the rest of the sentence.	

Try It!

Write two sentences with dialogue and quotation marks.

1. Answers will vary. _____

2. Answers will vary. _____

UNIT 5 Courage • **Lesson 4** *Martin Luther King, Jr.*

 ▶ **Dialogue**

Practice

Put quotation marks at the beginning and end of the character's words.

1. "I like the story about the horse," said Amber.

2. "Aren't you glad we know how to read and write?" asked Juan.

3. "I think she is a really good teacher," Lin declared.

4. "Yes! Without her, we wouldn't know how to read," said Scott.

5. "I agree," said Deana. "She is good! "

WRITER'S CRAFT

Sequence

Focus A good writer leads readers through a story.

> ▶ Following the sequence of events helps readers better understand a story.
> ▶ Looking for words that show time can help readers follow the sequence of events. Some examples of these words are: *first, then, later*.

Identify

Think about or reread "The Empty Pot." Write down four things that happened in the story. Write them in the order they happened.

1. **Answers will vary.** _____

_____

2. _____

_____

3. _____

_____

4. _____

_____

Sequence

Practice

Read this paragraph carefully. Then number the pictures in the correct sequence.

   Seth gets up every morning at seven o'clock. Every morning he does the same things. He gets dressed first. Then he makes his bed. After that he brushes his teeth. About fifteen minutes later, Seth is ready for breakfast.

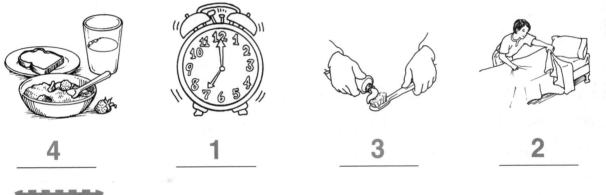

4 _____   1 _____   3 _____   2 _____

Apply

Write sentences about something you know how to do, such as making a sandwich, brushing your teeth, or walking to school. Make sure the sequence of events is clear.

Answers will vary.

_____

_____

_____

COMPREHENSION

Apostrophes and Colons

Apostrophes and **colons** are special punctuation marks.

Rule	**Example**
▶ An **apostrophe** is used to make a contraction.	▶ **It's** cold outside. [It is]
▶ An apostrophe is used to form the possessive.	▶ **Jay's** hat was black and gold.
▶ A **colon** is used to introduce a list of items.	▶ Please place these things in your suitcase: shoes, socks, shorts, and shirts.
▶ A colon is used in time expressions between the hour and the minutes.	▶ The bus is leaving at **2:45** sharp.

Write the time expression boldfaced in each sentence in numerals on the blank lines after the sentences.

1. At **two-ten**, the doors are locked. _____2:10_____

2. We must leave the house by **one-thirty**. _____1:30_____

▶ Apostrophes and Colons

Read the sentences. Find the words that need apostrophes and colons. Put the apostrophes and colons where they belong.

3. I couldn't agree with you more.

4. These are the best things in life:love, music, and friends.

5. A cat's life involves a lot of sleep.

6. My dog's favorite toy is my green tennis ball.

Write apostrophes and colons where they have been left out in the paragraph below. Use proofreading marks.

Britt's backpack was full. He had stuffed it with these things:three books, two notebooks, four pens, one pair of gloves, six tennis balls, and two sandwiches. He couldn't find his sandwiches. He was afraid that they might be crushed in the bottom of the backpack. Lunch break was at 11:45. He had to hurry to find his lunch.

MECHANICS

Sentence Combining

Two sentences with ideas that are alike can be put together or combined by using the word *and*.

Rules

▶ Put a comma before the word *and* when combining sentences.

▶ Do not use *and* to combine two sentences that are not about things that are alike.

Example

▶ Rosa walked to the mailbox, <u>and</u> she mailed the letter.

Try It!

Put an *X* next to the sentences that can be combined because they are on the same topic.

1. The dog barked. He wagged his tail. <u>X</u>

2. Jason ran home. The sun was shining. ___

3. Seth hit the ball. He ran to first base. <u>X</u>

4. The car was going fast. We were eating lunch. ___

5. Nick went to the phone. He answered it. <u>X</u>

UNIT 5 Courage • **Lesson 5** *The Empty Pot*

Combine these sentences by adding a comma and the word *and*.

1. The monkey jumped. It played.

The monkey jumped, and it played.

2. My dad and I went to the store. We bought tennis shoes.

My dad and I went to the store, and we bought tennis shoes.

3. Cathy peeled an orange. She ate it.

Cathy peeled an orange, and she ate it.

4. Marta climbed the steps. She slid down the slide.

Marta climbed the steps, and she slid down the slide.

5. The rabbit picked the carrot. He ate it.

The rabbit picked the carrot, and he ate it.

Author's Purpose

Focus Authors write for different reasons. Sometimes they want to give readers information. Sometimes they write to entertain.

> Writers *entertain* readers by including
> ▶ funny words and events
> ▶ exciting or familiar events
> Writers *inform* readers by including
> ▶ facts that can be proven true
> Writers *persuade* readers by including
> ▶ their opinions
> ▶ facts to support their opinions
> Writers *explain* to readers how to do something by including
> ▶ the steps in a process

Identify

Reread page 237 of "Brave As a Mountain Lion." What is the author's purpose?

Author's Purpose: **to entertain**

How did the author show the purpose? **Possible answer: bumpity-bump-bump went his heart**

▶ **Author's Purpose**

 **Practice**

Numbered below are some titles of stories. A list of purposes that authors can use is in the box. Choose the one that best fits each title.

| entertain | inform | persuade | explain |

1. "Why the School Year Should Be Longer"

persuade

2. "The Great Mahooleywhazit and the Big YUCK!"

entertain

3. "How to Feed a Baby"

explain

4. "Ocean Animals"

inform

 **Apply**

Choose one of the titles above and write a first sentence for the story. **Answers will vary.**

_____

_____

COMPREHENSION

UNIT 5 Courage • **Lesson 6** *Brave as a Mountain Lion*

Review

▶ Capitalization: I and Proper Nouns

Underline three times the words that should be capital letters.

1. This year i am taking ballet lessons.

2. One day i hope to dance like m. Tallchief.

3. She was part Native american and part scotch-irish.

▶ Conjunctions and Interjections

Underline the conjunctions and circle the interjections in the sentences below.

4. Maine and Vermont are states.

5. Gee! Is New York bordered by New Jersey or Massachusetts?

▶ Commas

Write commas where they are needed.

6. I asked the man, "Why isn't your brother going on the train trip?"

7. He said, "I hate hearing that clackety-clack!"

8. "I don't like airplanes," said Tommy.

Comprehension and Language Arts Skills

Review

MECHANICS

▶ **Capitalization**

Underline three times the letters that should be capitalized.

I am reading the book *Tiger's Stripes* by j. c. Cole. It is about a young tiger named Tiger jr. He is afraid he is going to lose his stripes if he goes swimming. Since he is afraid, he asks his owl friend, miss Howl. I wonder what he will do!

▶ **Apostrophes and Colons**

Insert colons and apostrophes where they belong in the sentences below.

9. Three islands are countries:Iceland, Greenland, and Australia.

10. Haven't you ever heard of Oceania?

11. The conductor said, "The train will depart at 6:15."

Time and Order Words

> ▶ You can show time in your writing by telling when things happen.
>
> ▶ Words such as *yesterday*, *tonight*, and *next week* show time.
>
> ▶ You can show order by telling in what order things happen.
>
> ▶ Words such as *first*, *next*, and *finally* show order.

Try It! **Write the time and order words in each sentence.**

1. Yesterday, we decided to buy some fish. **Yesterday**

2. First, we bought a fish tank. **First**

3. Then, we bought fish food. **Then**

4. Now, we are ready to pick our new pets. **Now**

5. Tonight, we will go to the pet store to buy

   the fish. **Tonight**

▶ **Time and Order Words**

Practice

Write a sentence using the time or order word next to each number.

6. Finally　　　　**Answers will vary.**

7. Next week　　**Answers will vary.**

8. First　　　　　**Answers will vary.**

9. Then　　　　　**Answers will vary.**

10. Tomorrow　　**Answers will vary.**

WRITER'S CRAFT

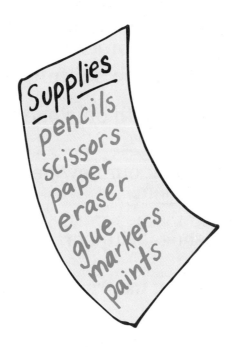

Supplies
pencils
scissors
paper
eraser
glue
markers
paints

Review

Common and Proper Nouns

Read the paragraph below. Circle the common nouns and underline the proper nouns.

There are many (types) of (trees). The Sequoias are one (type). They are named after a Cherokee (leader). In Arizona, the Petrified Forest is (home) to many old Sequoia (trees). The Coast Redwood, Giant Sequoia, and Dawn Redwood are all (types) of Sequoias.

Subject and Object Pronouns

Underline the subject pronouns and circle the object pronouns in these sentences.

1. They traveled the world with only one suitcase.

2. We wanted to be like (them).

3. She took too many shoes with (her).

4. Why can't he take (her) on his trip?

5. I don't want to go with (you).

► **Action Verbs**

Circle the action verbs in the sentences below.

6. Pioneers (clear) the land.

7. They (plant) seeds for corn.

8. They (dig) vegetable gardens.

9. The men and women (work) hard in the hot sun.

10. The children (help) their parents.

► **Possessive Nouns and Pronouns**

Read the sentences below. Fill in the correct possessive form in the blank.

11. _Seattle's_ name comes from a Native American tribal chief named Seattle. (**Seattle**)

12. _His_ tribal group was the Duwamish. (**He**)

13. The _city's_ location is in Washington. (**city**)

14. _Her_ brother likes to fish. (**She**)

Audience and Purpose

Your **audience** is the person or people reading your writing.

Your **purpose** is your reason for writing. There are four main purposes for writing.

Rule	**Example**
▶ To **inform** is to tell facts about something.	▶ China is the largest country.
▶ To **explain** is to tell how to do something or why something happens.	▶ Follow these steps to make a pizza.
▶ To **entertain** is to amuse people.	▶ The silly puppy fell asleep in the drawer.
▶ To **persuade** is to talk people into thinking or or doing something.	▶ Here is why we should not litter.

Try It! **After each sentence, write the purpose.**

1. If we all help, we can make our city clean. **persuade**

2. As the sun rose, the ocean sparkled like diamonds. **entertain**

3. Here are some simple steps to a better life. **explain**

4. This is the oldest fossil known to humans. **inform**

UNIT 6 Our Country and Its People • **Lesson I** *The First Americans*

▶ Audience and Purpose

WRITER'S CRAFT

Practice

For each type of writing, give a possible audience.

5. Fairy tale __children__

6. Directions to get to a friend's house

__a friend, a parent__

7. Report on United States history

__a teacher, someone new to the United States__

8. Poster for a school bake sale

__classmates, parents__

9. Article about a hockey game

__anyone who didn't see the game__

Cause and Effect

Focus When you read, the more you know about what caused something to happen, the better you will understand what you read.

Read the page from "New Hope." Then tell the cause of the event.

1. Page 269

   Event: Lars sailed with his family to this country from Denmark.

   Cause: **to start a new life in America**
   _____

2. Page 276

   Event: Lars opened a general store.

   Cause: **Lumber men and farmers came to live in**

   New Hope.

UNIT 6 Our Country and Its People • **Lesson 2** *New Hope*

Practice and Apply

For each of the events from "New Hope" listed below, write why it happened.

3. Page 270

Lars bought a wagon, two horses, a hunting rifle, tools, a tent, several bags of seeds, and plenty of food in Minnesota.

Why it happened: **Lars and his family were traveling further west in a wagon.**

4. Page 271

Peter and Mathilde adopted a dog.

Why it happened: **A dog appeared at the campsite; it was too far to take him back to the town they passed through earlier.**

5. Page 275

Franz opened a forge.

Why it happened: **The ferry landing was busy and that would bring lots of business.**

Review

Capitalization: Beginnings of Sentences; Months of the Year; Days of the Week

Commas: Words in a Series

Underline three times the letters that should be capitalized. Insert commas where they are needed.

1. The library will be closed on <u>s</u>undays, <u>m</u>ondays, and <u>t</u>uesdays this summer.

2. <u>o</u>wls live in trees, barns, or zoos.

3. Memorial Day is in the month of <u>m</u>ay.

4. Presidents' Day falls in <u>f</u>ebruary.

5. <u>w</u>hen is Father's Day?

6. <u>w</u>inter begins in <u>d</u>ecember in our country.

7. I take long walks on <u>t</u>uesdays, <u>t</u>hursdays, and <u>s</u>aturdays.

8. <u>t</u>he Midwest has long, cold winters.

9. We have fish, corn, and potatoes on <u>f</u>ridays.

10. School will be out in <u>j</u>une.

▶ **Capitalization and Commas in Greetings** ▶ Review

▶ **Commas in Closings; City, State, Date**

Read the letter. Insert commas where they are needed, and underline three times letters that should be capitalized.

626 Mason Drive
Albany, New York
july 1, 2001

dear Gerry,
   On Monday, I would like to borrow your flag.
I need your flag for the parade in our town. I
promise to take care of it!

Your cousin,
Amy

▶ **Quotation Marks and Underlining**

Read the sentences below. Add quotation marks and underlining where needed.

11. "Recycling helps the environment," said our
    teacher.

12. She read to us from a book titled Nature
    and the Environment.

13. I said, "We need to recycle our trash."

Words of Request

To get someone to do something, it helps to ask in a polite way. Words of request help you do this.

Words of Request:
- ▶ Please
- ▶ Could you
- ▶ Would you
- ▶ May I

Try It! **Circle the words of request in each sentence.**

1. (Would you) mind sending me a sample?

2. (Please) come to my party.

3. (May I) go to the movies?

4. (Could you) help me move the desk?

5. (May I)(please) have more information?

UNIT 6 Our Country and Its People • **Lesson 2** *New Hope*

► **Words of Request**

Practice

Write questions using words of request for each situation.

6. Ask for help with your homework.

   Answers will vary. _____

7. Ask your parents if they will let you stay the night at a friend's house.

   Answers will vary. _____

8. Ask a salesperson to refund your money.

   Answers will vary. _____

9. Ask someone to help you find your lost bike.

   Answers will vary. _____

10. Ask for help lifting something heavy.

   Answers will vary. _____

WRITER'S CRAFT

▶ **Kinds of Sentences**

Read each sentence below. Insert the correct end mark. Then write *D* if the sentence is a statement. Write *Q* if the sentence asks a question. Write *I* if the sentence gives a direction or a command. Write *E* if the sentence is an exclamatory sentence.

1. Don't rock the boat. ___I___

2. Where is your life jacket? ___Q___

3. The water is blue and calm today. ___D___

4. Look how far we can see across the lake! ___E___

▶ **Linking and Helping Verbs**

Underline the linking verbs and circle the helping verbs in each sentence.

5. Texas <u>is</u> not the largest state.

6. In 1959 it <u>was</u> the largest state.

7. Then Alaska (was) made a state.

8. Now Alaska <u>is</u> the largest state.

▶Review

GRAMMAR AND USAGE

▶Subject/Verb Agreement

Correct the underlined verbs so they agree with the subjects.

The Sahara Desert ~~are~~ *is* the largest in the world. It ~~are~~ *is* in Africa. The word *Sahara* is Arabic for *desert*. Not many plants ~~grows~~ *grow* in the Sahara.

▶Parts of Sentences

Underline the subject once and the predicate twice.

9. My great-grandmother came to this country on a ship.

10. They brought food with them for the trip.

▶Complete Sentences

Change the run-on phrases into a complete sentence.

11. Tokyo capital of Japan.

   Tokyo is the capital of Japan.

UNIT 6 Our Country and Its People • **Lesson 3** *A Place Called Freedom*

Structure of Scripts

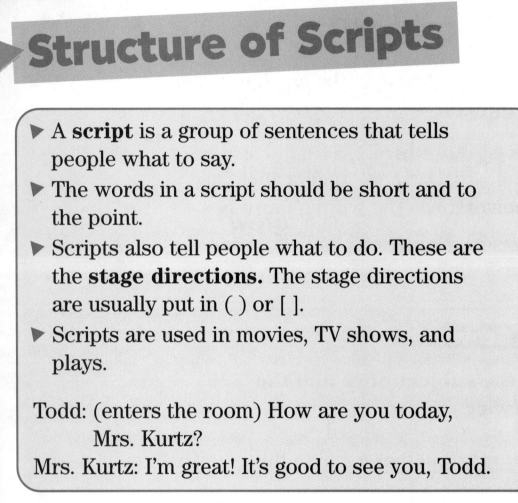

▶ A **script** is a group of sentences that tells people what to say.

▶ The words in a script should be short and to the point.

▶ Scripts also tell people what to do. These are the **stage directions.** The stage directions are usually put in ( ) or [ ].

▶ Scripts are used in movies, TV shows, and plays.

Todd: (enters the room) How are you today, Mrs. Kurtz?

Mrs. Kurtz: I'm great! It's good to see you, Todd.

 **Read the script lines. Circle the letter of the line that is short and to the point.**

1. **A.** It seemed like we had to walk forever and ever.
   B. We walked for a long time.

2. **A.** The train is late!
   B. I can't believe the train is not running on time!

3. **A.** I wanted to ask you if you have seen Carlos today.
   B. Have you seen Carlos today?

▶ Structure of Scripts

Write a short script for the following example. Add stage directions.

Example: Dan and Zack are talking about last night's homework.

Dan: **Answers will vary.** _____

Zack: **Answers will vary.** _____

Dan: **Answers will vary.** _____

Zack: **Answers will vary.** _____

WRITER'S CRAFT

Review

Adjectives and Adverbs

Circle the adjectives and underline the adverbs in the sentences below.

1. The (red) lines on the map are highways.

2. (Black) dots <u>usually</u> represent cities.

3. Capitals are <u>clearly</u> shown with (white) stars.

4. There are (fifty) states on the map.

5. The map uses (five) colors for the states.

Circle the articles in the following sentences.

6. Green trees are (the) symbol for parks.

7. (The) brown triangles mean tall mountains.

8. There was (a) red square for (a) school.

9. Fold (the) map carefully.

10. I used (an) orange marker to highlight our trip.

▶Review

▶ **Contractions**

Circle the correct contraction to complete each sentence.

11. My dog **hasn't'** (**hasn't**) been fed yet today.

12. **Its** (**It's**) too late to call Grandma now.

13. We (**didn't**) **didnt** find the treasure.

14. I (**wasn't**) **wast'n** sure where to look.

15. (**You're**) **your** my favorite teacher.

GRAMMAR AND USAGE

UNIT 6 Kindness • **Lesson 5** *The Butterfly Seeds*

Making Inferences

Focus Sometimes a writer gives us hints about an event in the story or about what a character is thinking and feeling. These hints can help readers make inferences.

> ▶ A reader makes an **inference** by using information from the story and information that the reader knows from his or her experience.

Identify

Read the sentence from "The Butterfly Seeds." Then write the inference you can make from this information.

Jake's house was empty, except for the overstuffed trunk in the middle of the floor.

Inference: **Jake's family is moving.** _____

_____

Practice

Read each statement on the following page. Write the inference you can make from each statement.

▶**Making Inferences**

After we ate a piece of cake, my brother began opening his gifts.

Inference: **It is his birthday.**

_____

Are we playing that game again?

Inference: **This person has played the same game recently.**

Look through "The Butterfly Seeds" or any story you have already read. Find a sentence that hints at something without really telling you. Write the sentence and tell what inference you can make.

Sentence: **Answers will vary.**

_____

Inference: _____

_____

Review

Linking and Helping Verb Tenses

Circle the present tense verbs and underline the past tense verbs in the sentences below.

1. We (are talking) on the phone with the librarian.

2. There (are) some new books in the library.

3. I <u>have returned</u> the old library books.

4. Who (is) the author of this animal story?

5. He <u>had given</u> it to me last week.

Look at the verbs you circled and underlined above. Write linking or helping on the line number for each sentence.

6. _____helping_____

7. _____linking_____

8. _____helping_____

9. _____linking_____

10. _____helping_____

UNIT 6 Our Country and Its People • **Lesson 5** *The Butterfly Seeds*

Singular and Plural Nouns

Circle the singular nouns and underline the plural nouns in each sentence.

11. How many <u>giraffes</u> are in the (zoo)?

12. They say that a (cat) has nine <u>lives</u>.

13. The (house) has five <u>windows</u>.

14. There are two full <u>moons</u> this (month).

15. Put the <u>toys</u> for (charity) in these two <u>boxes</u>.

Adverbs

Read the following paragraph. Underline the adverbs.

The violin is part of the string family of instruments. <u>Yesterday</u>, I learned that the viola, cello, and double bass are <u>also</u> part of the violin family. Harmonics can be played by <u>lightly</u> placing your hand on the strings. Orchestras <u>always</u> have violins in them.

GRAMMAR AND USAGE

Words of Request

> To get someone to do something, it helps to ask in a polite way. Words of request help you do this.
>
> Words of Request:
> ▶ Please
> ▶ Could you
> ▶ Would you
> ▶ May I

 **Underline the words of request in each sentence.**

1. May I please have a piece of the apple?

2. Could you help me carry my books?

3. May I stay up until 10:00 tonight?

4. Please bring muffins to the bake sale.

5. Would you ask if I could go too?

Words of Request

Practice

Write five questions using words of request.

6. Answers will vary.

7. Answers will vary.

8. Answers will vary.

9. Answers will vary.

10. Answers will vary.

WRITER'S CRAFT

UNIT 6 Our Country and Its People • **Lesson 6** *A Piece of Home*

Review

Capitalization: *I*, Proper Nouns, People's Titles and Initials

Underline three times the letters that should be capitalized.

1. Today i read a book about the american Revolution.

2. The british army was one of the best in the world.

3. Congress asked general George washington to lead the troops.

Conjunctions and Interjections

Circle the conjunctions and underline the interjections in the sentences below.

4. The Snake River flows westward,(and)the Missouri River flows eastward.

5. Oh! I forgot to study geography last night.

6. Do it this morning(or)at lunchtime.

MECHANICS

▶**Review**

▶ **Commas in Dialogue**

Add commas where they belong in each sentence.

7. I told the captain‸"Aye, aye, sir."

8. G. M. Cohan said‸"I'm a Yankee Doodle Dandy."

9. "I saw a great movie last night‸" explained Timothy.

▶ **Apostrophes**

Insert apostrophes where they belong in each sentence.

10. Switzerlands mountains are beautiful.

11. We couldnt climb to the very top.

12. The countrys people speak three languages.

▶ **Colons**

Write colons where they belong in each sentence.

13. My favorite television program starts at 5‸00.

14. These animals were in the show‸dogs, pigs, cats, and birds.

15. I will be leaving at 4‸45 today.

Supporting Details

> ▶ The **main idea** is the topic of the paragraph.
> ▶ **Supporting details** tell about the main idea.
>
> Main Idea: Hawaii is a beautiful place.
> Details:
> ▶ The beaches are breathtaking.
> ▶ There are grand mountains.
> ▶ Hawaii has colorful trees and flowers.

 **Read the main idea below. Then cross out the one sentence that does not tell about the main idea.**

Main Idea: Toby is a smart dog.

Details: • He fetches the newspaper every morning.
• ~~Toby is a black lab.~~
• He can catch a biscuit in the air.
• He can push the button on an elevator for the correct floor.

▶ Supporting Details

Write three details about the main idea below.

Main Idea: There is a lot to do in the winter.

Answers will vary.

_____

_____

_____

_____

_____

_____

_____

WRITER'S CRAFT

Fact and Opinion

Focus Writers talk to readers through their stories. To make their stories interesting, writers use facts and opinions.

> ▶ A **fact** is something that can be proven true. It is a fact that jalapeños grow on plants.
>
> ▶ An **opinion** is what someone thinks or feels. It is an opinion if someone says jalapeños taste good.

Identify

Look back at "Jalapeño Bagels." Copy one sentence that gives a fact. Copy one sentence that gives an opinion. **Answers will vary.**

Fact

1. _____

_____

Opinion

2. _____

_____

▶ **Fact and Opinion**

Read this paragraph. Draw a line under each sentence that tells a fact. Circle the sentences that give opinions.

Jamie was born in the United States. His parents were born in Mexico. They moved to the United States ten years ago. His parents are wonderful. They have taught him how to speak two languages. It is important to know more than one language. That way he can talk to more people.

Write several sentences about your favorite food. Make sure you include some facts and some opinions.

Answers will vary.

_____

_____

_____

_____

_____

COMPREHENSION

UNIT 6 Our Country and Its People • **Lesson 7** *Jalapeño Bagels*

▶ **Sentences: End Marks**

▶ **Subjects and Predicates**

Circle the subject and underline the predicate in the sentences below. Then, add the correct end mark.

1. (Many Irish people in the 1800s) relied on potatoes for food.

2. (Their crops) failed so many times!

▶ **Common and Proper Nouns**

Circle the common nouns and underline the proper nouns in these sentences.

3. Panda (bears) live in China.

4. China has loaned the United States two (bears).

▶ **Plural Nouns**

Circle the correct plural noun from the two boldfaced words in each sentence.

5. All the (**children**) **childs** helped in the garden.

6. The (**boys**) **boyes** raked the dirt.

Name _____ Date _____

▶**Review**

▶ **Linking and Action Verbs**

▶ **Present and Past Tense**

Look at the word in boldface. Circle *Past* or *Present* at the end of each sentence.

7. People **were playing** board games 4,000 years ago. (Past) **Present**

8. Chess **is played** with figures of the king, queen, and bishop. (Present) **Past**

▶ **Adjectives and Adverbs**

Circle the adjectives and underline the adverbs in each sentence.

9. (Yellow) parakeets make (nice) pets.

10. (Many) birds sing beautifully.

▶ **Contractions and Conjunctions**

Circle the contractions and underline the conjunctions in the sentences.

11. Games and sports take practice to learn.

12. Many sports (aren't) easy to master.

Plagiarism

> **Plagiarism** is using someone else's ideas or statements as your own. It is important that you write papers using your own words.

 **Rewrite each sentence in your own words.**

1. The largest animal that lives on land is the African elephant.

Answers will vary.

_____

2. The fastest land animal, the cheetah, runs at 70 miles per hour.

Answers will vary.

_____

3. In the desert lives the bobcat.

Answers will vary.

_____

 **Plagiarism**

Practice

Read the paragraph. Then rewrite it in your own words.

Pluto is the smallest planet. It is much smaller than the other planets. It is 1,413 miles wide. That may not seem very small, but compare it to the biggest planet, Jupiter. It is 88,732 miles wide. Pluto is also the coldest planet. It is so cold that nothing could live there.

Answers will vary.

_____

_____

_____

_____

WRITER'S CRAFT